Workbook
Auto Suspension and Steering

by

Chris Johanson
ASE Certified Master Technician

Publisher
The Goodheart-Willcox Company, Inc.
Tinley Park, Illinois
www.g-w.com

The Goodheart-Willcox Company, Inc. Brand Disclaimer: Brand names, company names, and illustrations for products and services included in this text are provided for educational purposes only and do not represent or imply endorsement or recommendation by the author or the publisher.

The Goodheart-Willcox Company, Inc. Safety Notice: The reader is expressly advised to carefully read, understand, and apply all safety precautions and warnings described in this book or that might also be indicated in undertaking the activities and exercises described herein to minimize risk of personal injury or injury to others. Common sense and good judgment should also be exercised and applied to help avoid all potential hazards. The reader should always refer to the appropriate manufacturer's technical information, directions, and recommendations; then proceed with care to follow specific equipment operating instructions. The reader should understand these notices and cautions are not exhaustive.

The publisher makes no warranty or representation whatsoever, either expressed or implied, including but not limited to equipment, procedures, and applications described or referred to herein, their quality, performance, merchantability, or fitness for a particular purpose. The publisher assumes no responsibility for any changes, errors, or omissions in this book. The publisher specifically disclaims any liability whatsoever, including any direct, indirect, incidental, consequential, special, or exemplary damages resulting, in whole or in part, from the reader's use or reliance upon the information, instructions, procedures, warnings, cautions, applications, or other matter contained in this book. The publisher assumes no responsibility for the activities of the reader.

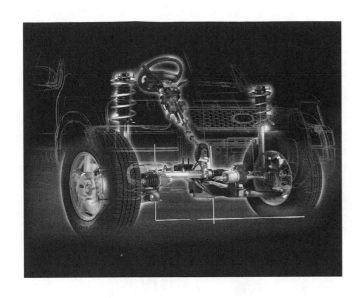

Table of Contents

Jobs

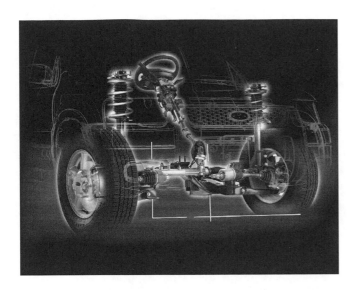

Introduction

The **Workbook for Auto Suspension and Steering** is designed to reinforce your understanding of the important information presented in the textbook. To accomplish this, the workbook utilizes several types of questions and illustration exercises to highlight key aspects relating to the operation, construction, design, maintenance, troubleshooting, and repair of the suspension and steering systems found on late-model cars and light trucks.

As in the textbook, a list of objectives is provided at the beginning of each workbook chapter to summarize what should be learned. Each question in the workbook is presented in a manner that measures your comprehension of important topics. The workbook's illustration exercises are visual learning tools that help you understand system and component construction, as well as maintenance, troubleshooting, and repair procedures.

The workbook chapters correlate to the corresponding chapters in the textbook. The order of the questions in each chapter follows the sequence of the textbook material. This makes it easier for you to find information in the text and to check your answers. It is recommended that you study the assigned chapters in the **Auto Suspension and Steering** textbook before you attempt to answer questions in this workbook. After studying the textbook, try to answer as many of the corresponding workbook questions as possible without referring to the text. Answer any remaining questions by referring to the appropriate areas in the textbook chapters.

The jobs contained in this workbook are hands-on activities in component inspection, testing, problem diagnostics, service, and repair. They are designed to give you a chance to apply what you have learned throughout **Auto Suspension and Steering.** The workbook jobs are not correlated to the text, but will be assigned when your instructor decides you have sufficient knowledge to complete them. When performing the tasks in the jobs, follow instructions carefully and proceed through the task steps in the order they are presented. Record the results of all diagnostic procedures whenever required.

This workbook, when used to supplement the **Auto Suspension and Steering** textbook, will help you become a successful suspension and steering technician.

Chris Johanson

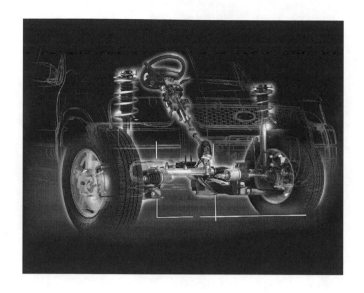

Instructions for Answering Workbook Questions

Each chapter in this workbook correlates to a corresponding chapter in the textbook. Before answering the questions in the workbook, study the assigned chapter in the text and answer the end-of-chapter review questions. Then, review the objectives at the beginning of each workbook chapter. This will help you recall the important concepts presented in the chapter. Try to complete as many workbook questions as possible without referring to the textbook. Then, use the text to complete the remaining questions.

A variety of questions are used in the workbook, including multiple choice, completion, identification, and short answer. These questions should be answered in the following manner:

Multiple Choice

Select the best answer and write the correct letter in the blank.

1. To remove a conventional shock absorber, which of the following parts must be removed?
   (A) Control arm.
   (B) Coil spring.
   (C) Torsion bar.
   (D) None of the above.

1. *D*

Completion

In the blank provided, write the word or words that best complete the statement.

2. Slip yokes are used on _____-wheel drive vehicles.

2. *rear*

Identification

Identify the components indicated on the illustration or photograph accompanying the question.

3. Identify the indicated components of the MacPherson strut assembly shown below.

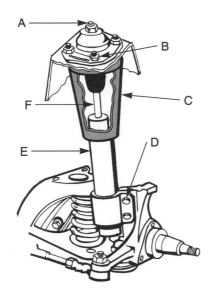

3. (A) *Piston rod nut*

   (B) *Upper mounting nuts*

   (C) *Dust cover*

   (D) *Lower mounting nuts and bolts*

   (E) *Strut*

   (F) *Piston rod*

Short Answer

Provide complete responses to the questions.

4. What is the purpose of the dust boot mounted over the MacPherson strut piston rod?

   The dust boot protects the piston rod from water and dirt.

Other Types of Questions

When other types of workbook questions are presented, follow the specific instructions that accompany the questions.

Instructions for Completing the Workbook Job Sheets

Before starting any job, complete the related textbook and workbook chapters. Read the objective and instructions for the job. Ask your instructor for any possible changes in the job procedures and for help as needed. Read and complete each step of the job carefully while observing all safety rules. Be sure to answer all questions and record the results of all diagnostic procedures when required.

Chapter 1

Basic Suspension and Steering Systems Operation

After studying this chapter, you will be able to:
- ❏ Explain why vehicles require suspension and steering systems.
- ❏ Identify various suspension and steering systems.
- ❏ Explain how the suspension and steering systems interact with other vehicle systems.
- ❏ Identify types of vehicle body and frame construction.
- ❏ Describe vehicle drive train systems.

1. To improve comfort and handling, a vehicle's suspension system must absorb _____ _____.

1. _____

2. Early automotive suspensions used _____ springs.

2. _____

3. By the 1940s, most front suspensions had _____ springs. This design was unchanged for many years, except for the occasional use of _____ bars and the introduction of _____ joints. Most cars had _____-wheel drive, and the rear axle was a(n) _____ type.

3. _____
_____
_____
_____
_____
_____
_____

4. By the late 1960s, _____ _____ suspension was being used in many small vehicles, especially on the front axle.

4. _____

5. Two drive systems that were once rare but have become common during the last two decades are _____-wheel drive systems and _____-wheel drive systems.

5. _____
_____

6. All manufacturers used the _____ steering linkage during the 1950s and 1960s. It was gradually replaced by the _____-_____-_____ steering system.

6. _____
_____

Name _____

7. Technician A says the top of a MacPherson strut is usually fastened to the vehicle's body. Technician B says the bottom of the strut is usually attached to the control arm. Who is right?
   (A) A only.
   (B) B only.
   (C) Both A and B.
   (D) Neither A nor B.

7. _____

8. All the following statements about shock absorbers are true *except:*
   (A) shock absorbers reduce spring oscillations.
   (B) shock absorbers absorb some road shock.
   (C) shock absorbers work by expanding then slowly compressing.
   (D) some shock absorbers are installed inside of the coil spring.

8. _____

9. Control arms always have two frame bushings. True or False?

9. _____

10. Strut rods provide extra _____.

10. _____

11. Identify the components of the MacPherson strut assembly shown below.

(A) _____

(B) _____

(C) _____

(D) _____

(E) _____

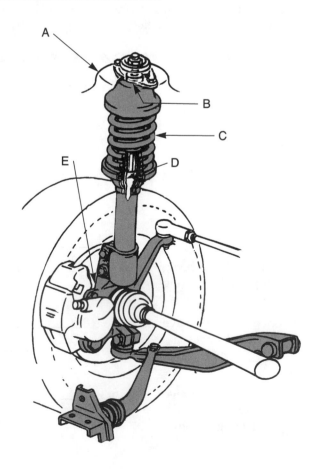

Name _____

12. Sway bars keep the vehicle level during _____.   12. _____

13. Identify the components of the short-long arm (SLA), or conventional, front suspension assembly shown below.

(A) _____   (F) _____

(B) _____   (G) _____

(C) _____   (H) _____

(D) _____   (I) _____

(E) _____

14. Independent rear suspensions usually use _____   14. _____
    springs or MacPherson struts. A few independent rear
    suspensions use _____ _____ instead of springs.   _____

                                                               _____

15. Which of the following are *not* used on solid rear   15. _____
    axles?
    (A) Coil springs
    (B) MacPherson struts
    (C) Leaf springs
    (D) All are used on solid rear axles.

16. The size of the steering wheel is designed to create as   16. _____
    much _____ _____ as possible without being too large
    to operate.

17. In a rack-and-pinion system, the rack and pinion have   17. _____
    meshing _____. The rack is connected to the steering
    linkage through _____ _____.   _____

18. The conventional steering gearbox contains a(n)   18. _____
    _____ and a(n) _____ gear. The gearbox is connected
    to the steering linkage through a(n) _____ arm.   _____

                                                               _____

                                                               _____

19. Power steering systems use _____ pressure to assist   19. _____
    the driver.

20. On a body-over-frame vehicle, the frame and body   20. _____
    are _____ together.

21. On a unibody vehicle, the frame and body are _____   21. _____
    into a single unit.

Name _____

22. Modern unibody vehicles are designed to be rigid in the _____ _____ area. The crumple zones are located at the _____ and rear _____.

22. _____

_____

_____

23. Vehicle stability increases when the center of gravity is _____.

23. _____

❑   Match the following statements with the type of drive they describe.

24. Most use two CV axles.

(A) Front-wheel drive.

24. _____

25. May have a center support.

(B) Rear-wheel drive.

25. _____

26. Use U-joints.

(C) Four-wheel drive.

26. _____

27. May have an intermediate shaft.

27. _____

28. Has a transfer case.

28. _____

29. Most often used with a transverse engine.

29. _____

30. Which of the following is *not* an input to the electronic steering or suspension system?
    (A) Solenoid.
    (B) Steering wheel position sensor.
    (C) Load sensor.
    (D) Throttle position sensor.

30. _____

Chapter 2

Shop Safety and Environmental Protection

After studying this chapter, you will be able to:
- ❑ Identify the major causes of accidents in the workplace.
- ❑ Explain why accidents must be avoided.
- ❑ Describe ways to maintain a safe work area.
- ❑ List safe work procedures.
- ❑ Identify types of environmental damage caused by improper auto shop practices.
- ❑ Help prevent environmental damage by discarding automotive wastes properly.

1. Even experienced technicians can become rushed and _____.

1. _____

2. List three types of injuries caused by accidents in the auto repair shop.

_____

_____

3. What can happen in the shop to cause long-term bodily harm?

_____

_____

4. Give an example of long-term bodily harm that can occur as a result of the actions listed in question 3.

_____

5. List three ways to prevent accidents in the auto repair shop.

_____

_____

_____

_____

6. Briefly explain why it is important to determine whether a part is under spring tension before the part is removed.

_____

_____

_____

7. Why is it important to clean up gasoline spills immediately?

_____

_____

8. A(n) _____-_____ lightbulb should always be used in an incandescent droplight.

8. _____

9. Equipment should never be operated without proper safety _____ in place.

9. _____

10. Technician A says any piece of shop equipment should be turned off and unplugged before it is serviced. Technician B says there is an MSDS for every piece of equipment in the shop. Who is right?
   (A) A only
   (B) B only.
   (C) Both A and B.
   (D) Neither A nor B.

10. _____

11. All the following statements about fire extinguishers are true *except:*
   (A) you should know how to operate the fire extinguishers found in your shop.
   (B) you should know where the fire extinguishers are located.
   (C) you should know what type of fire extinguisher is needed for each type of fire.
   (D) you should know how to recharge fire extinguishers.

11. _____

12. A Class _____ fire extinguisher should be used to put out an electrical fire.

12. _____

13. All the following are ways in which a technician could accidentally start a fire in the shop *except:*
   (A) using a jumper wire to create a short circuit.
   (B) spilling antifreeze.
   (C) spilling gasoline.
   (D) smoking in the shop.

13. _____

14. Always lift with your _____, not your _____.

14. _____

_____

15. If technicians and other members of the public ignore waste and dumping laws, who will have to deal with the problem?

15. _____

16. What is a core value?

_____

_____

Name _____

17. Antifreeze, brake fluid, and petroleum products should never be poured on the ground or into _____.

17. _____

18. Liquid wastes sink into the ground and can contaminate the local source of _____ water.

18. _____

19. Used oil and antifreeze can be _____ and then reused.

19. _____

20. Which of the following is enforced by the Environmental Protection Agency (EPA)?
    (A) Federal job safety laws.
    (B) Federal vehicle emissions laws.
    (C) Federal wage and hour laws.
    (D) Federal hiring laws in the automotive industry.

20. _____

Chapter 3

Special Service Tools and Equipment

After studying this chapter, you will be able to:
- ❑ Identify common suspension and steering hand tools and explain their use.
- ❑ Identify alignment equipment and related tools and explain their use.
- ❑ Identify safety and personal protective equipment.
- ❑ List general rules for the correct use and storage of tools.
- ❑ Cite tool safety rules and explain where they apply.
- ❑ Select the proper tool for the job at hand.

1. Many ball joint and tie rod end removal tools, steering wheel pullers, and pitman arm pullers rely on a central _____ that is tightened to force the components apart.

1. _____

2. Technician A says the MacPherson strut compressor is used to compress the spring before the strut assembly is removed from the vehicle. Technician B says the MacPherson strut compressor must be used before a MacPherson strut can be disassembled. Who is right?
   (A) A only.
   (B) B only.
   (C) Both A and B.
   (D) Neither A nor B.

2. _____

3. A bushing installation tool used with a hammer is called a bushing _____. Other bushing installation tools resemble large _____.

3. _____

   _____

Name _____

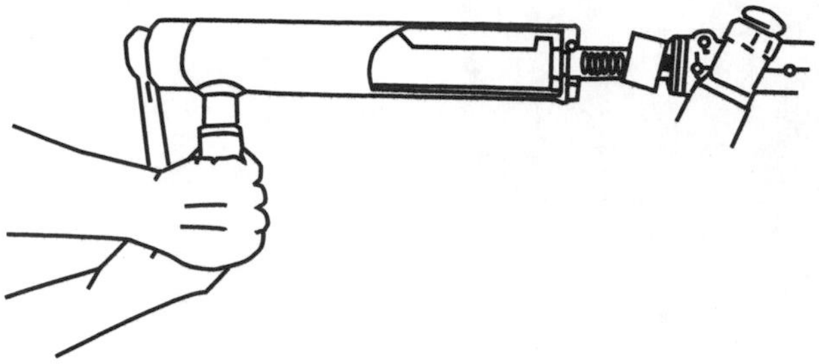

4. Technician A says the illustration above shows an inner tie rod being removed. Technician B says the illustration above shows an outer tie rod being removed. Who is right?
(A) A only.
(B) B only.
(C) Both A and B.
(D) Neither A nor B.

4. _____

5. Torque sticks are used with what type of wrench?

5. _____

6. In addition to cutting away body metal, what other jobs can a grinder be used for?

_____

_____

_____

7. If a vehicle with power steering is hard to turn, the technician might use any of the following tools for diagnosis except:
(A) belt tension gauge.
(B) steering effort gauge.
(C) power steering pressure gauge.
(D) air pressure gauge.

7. _____

8. Most power steering pressure gauges have a range of 0 to _____ psi (_____ kPa).

8. _____

_____

9. The tool shown below is used to adjust the steering linkage adjuster _____.

9. _____

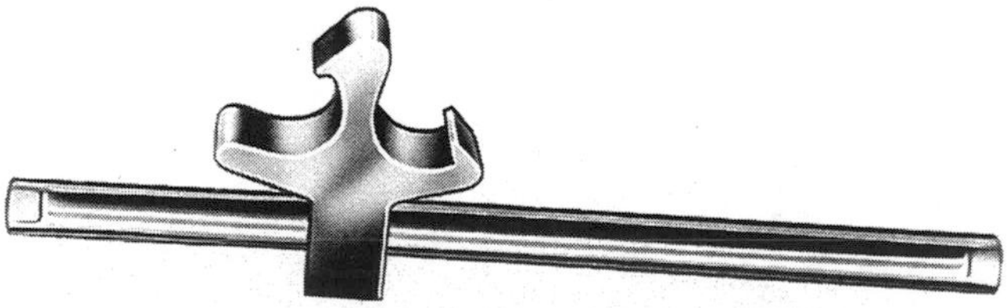

10. A battery-powered test light is used to determine whether a circuit is _____.

10. _____

11. Resistance is measured in _____. Current is measured in _____.

11. _____

_____

12. In addition to their other functions, some _____ can display waveforms.

12. _____

13. A special tester used to diagnose the steering and suspension systems of one manufacturer only is called a(n) _____ tester.

13. _____

Name _____

14. Which of the following alignment devices requires
    the most time and attention to obtain the correct
    alignment?
    (A) Light beam alignment machine.
    (B) Mechanical alignment equipment.
    (C) Electronic alignment machine.
    (D) Computerized alignment equipment.

14. _____

15. The tool illustrated below can be used to check
    _____.
    (A) toe-in
    (B) toe-out
    (C) camber
    (D) None of the above.

15. _____

Tool

16. _____ _____ allow the wheels to be turned easily
    during caster checks.

16. _____

17. Most tire changing machines have a(n) _____ breaker
    and a device for _____ the tire.

17. _____
    _____

18. The most common type of wheel balancer is used
    with the tire _____ the vehicle.

18. _____

19. The technician should always wear _____ _____
    when operating a hydraulic press.

19. _____

20. A steam cleaner should be used carefully, since steam
    can damage _____ _____ and _____ _____.

20. _____
    _____

21. After suspension and steering parts have been
    removed from the vehicle, they can be cleaned in a(n)
    _____ _____.

21. _____

22. What causes a hydraulic jack to lower when the oper-
    ator releases the hydraulic pressure?
    (A) Reverse hydraulic pressure.
    (B) Spring pressure.
    (C) Jack rolling action.
    (D) Vehicle weight.

22. _____

23. An above-ground lift does *not* have _____ _____ in
    the floor of the service bay.

23. _____

24. The steering wheel lock is used to make sure the
    steering wheel is _____ during alignment.

24. _____

Name _____

25. All the following tools would be used during a wheel alignment *except:*
    (A) tie rod turning tool.
    (B) brake pedal lock.
    (C) bushing installer
    (D) steering wheel lock.

25. _____

26. _____ service manuals contain the information needed to repair one manufacturer's vehicles.

26. _____

27. _____ manuals generally cover one common system for one vehicle or for many types of vehicles.

27. _____

28. A _____ is a graphic representation of a hydraulic, pneumatic, or electrical system.

28. _____

Name_____

Date _____ Instructor_____

Score_____ Textbook pages 67–84

Chapter 4

Common Suspension System Components

After studying this chapter, you will be able to:
- ❑ Identify and explain the operation of modern vehicle springs.
- ❑ Explain the operation of various types of shock absorbers.
- ❑ Explain the purpose of control arms and strut rods.
- ❑ Explain the purpose of steering knuckles.
- ❑ Explain the operation of ball joints and identify ball joint load types.
- ❑ Explain the purpose and design of bushings.
- ❑ Explain the operation of stabilizer bars.
- ❑ Identify modern drive train types and explain how the drive train type affects suspension design.
- ❑ Identify modern frame types and explain how the frame type affects suspension design.

1. Springs convert sharp jolts into soft _____.

2. The body and control arm depressions used to hold coil springs in place are called spring _____.

1. _____

2. _____

3. The coil spring illustrated above is called a(n) _____-_____ spring.

4. Describe the purpose of a leaf spring shackle.

3. _____

_____

_____

_____

Name _____

5. A transverse spring is mounted _____ to the vehicle's centerline.

5. _____

6. Transverse leaf springs are being discussed. Technician A says transverse leaf springs are sometimes used on front-wheel drive vehicles. Technician B says transverse leaf springs are often made of a material other than metal. Who is right?
   (A) A only.
   (B) B only.
   (C) Both A and B.
   (D) Neither A nor B.

6. _____

7. Each of the following statements about torsion bars is true *except:*
   (A) one end of a torsion bar is attached to the vehicle's body.
   (B) most torsion bars are mounted longitudinally.
   (C) torsion bars absorb shocks by twisting.
   (D) all torsion bars are adjustable.

7. _____

8. Torsion bars adjustments change vehicle _____ _____.

8. _____

9. Is the leaf spring in the illustration below a single- or multiple-leaf type?

9. _____

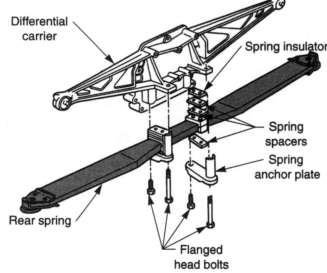

Differential carrier

Spring insulator

Spring spacers

Spring anchor plate

Rear spring

Flanged head bolts

10. Is the leaf spring in the above illustration a longitudinal or transverse spring?

10. _____

11. In an air spring system, air-operated _____ are used in place of coil springs or leaf springs.

11. _____

12. All modern shock absorbers are _____ _____.

12. _____

13. A shock absorber damps road shocks and oscillations by forcing hydraulic fluid through small _____.

13. _____

14. Shock absorbers are generally mounted to the suspension and frame through _____.

14. _____

15. The gas used in air shock absorbers is usually _____.

15. _____

Name _____

16. Adding air to an air shock increases pressure on the _____ _____, causing it to raise the vehicle.

16. _____

17. An A-arm type control arm is attached to a vehicle's body at how many places? _____ At how many places is it attached to the spindle? _____

17. _____
_____

18. Strut rods keep the control arms from moving _____.
(A) up and down
(B) backward and forward
(C) in and out
(D) None of the above.

18. _____

19. The steering knuckle may be called the _____ _____.

19. _____

20. A driving knuckle has a center hole that allows the _____ to pass through.

20. _____

21. The ball joint connects the _____ _____ to the _____ _____.

21. _____
_____

22. A two-piece ball joint provides an extra _____ surface.

22. _____

23. What three ways can a ball joint be attached to the control arm?

_____

_____

_____

24. How is a ball joint lubricated if it has no grease fitting?
(A) By lifting up the seal and squirting in grease.
(B) Using a needle to puncture the seal.
(C) Drilling a small hole and adding grease by hand.
(D) None of the above.

24. _____

25. Preloading keeps the ball joint surfaces from _____ each other when the suspension moves. This reduces _____ _____ and _____.

25. _____
_____
_____

26. The ball joint shown in the following illustration is _____ loaded.

26. _____

27. A(n) _____ bushing works by twisting.

27. _____

28. A stabilizer bar is sometimes called a(n) _____ bar.

28. _____

Name _____

29. A stabilizer bar is connected through bushings to all the following vehicle components *except:*
   (A) right lower control arm.
   (B) vehicle frame or body.
   (C) strut rod bushings.
   (D) left lower control arm.

29.

30. Technician A says the bushing shown in the following illustration is often used as a control arm bushing. Technician B says the bushing shown in the following illustration works by being compressed. Who is right?
   (A) A only.
   (B) B only.
   (C) Both A and B.
   (D) Neither A nor B.

30. _____

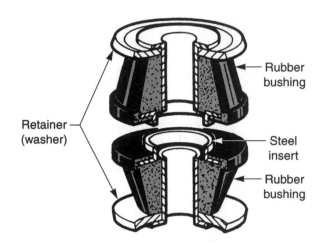

Name_____

Date _____ Instructor_____

Score_____ Textbook pages 85–102

Chapter 5
Front Suspension Systems

After studying this chapter, you will be able to:
- ❑ Explain the operation of MacPherson strut front suspensions.
- ❑ Identify the components of MacPherson strut front suspensions.
- ❑ Explain the operation of conventional front suspensions.
- ❑ Identify the components of conventional front suspensions.
- ❑ Explain the operation of solid and I-beam front suspensions.
- ❑ Identify the components of solid and I-beam front suspensions.
- ❑ Identify loaded and follower ball joints in both MacPherson strut and conventional front suspension systems.

1. The upper MacPherson strut mounting is sometimes called the strut _____. It is a steel plate contoured to fit a matching spot on the vehicle's _____. The top of the _____ rod passes through this plate.

2. Since the entire strut assembly _____ with the wheels, a bearing or a flexible rubber mount must be used at the upper mounting.

3. The lower MacPherson strut mounting is attached to the _____ _____.

4. To keep the MacPherson strut assembly from being compressed too much, a(n) _____ is used. To keep the MacPherson strut assembly from extending too far, a(n) _____ _____ is used.

1. _____
   _____
   _____
   _____

2. _____

3. _____

4. _____
   _____

5. What is the purpose of the dust boot mounted over the MacPherson strut piston rod?

_____

_____

Name _____

6. Technician A says the spring is separate from the strut in a few MacPherson strut suspensions. Technician B says some MacPherson strut assemblies have additional springs for extra control. Who is right?
   (A) A only.
   (B) B only.
   (C) Both A and B.
   (D) Neither A nor B.

6. _____

7. A multilink suspension is a modified type of _____ suspension.
   (A) conventional coil spring
   (B) conventional torsion bar
   (C) solid front axle
   (D) MacPherson strut

7. _____

8. Identify the indicated components of the MacPherson strut assembly shown below.

(A) _____   (D) _____

(B) _____   (E) _____

(C) _____   (F) _____

9. All _____ independent front suspensions use the short-long arm design.

9. _____

Name _____

10. The illustration below shows a_____.   10. _____
   (A) MacPherson strut with an internal spring and a
        coil spring helper
   (B) MacPherson strut with a separate spring
   (C) conventional suspension with a coil spring on
        the upper control arm
   (D) conventional suspension with a coil spring on
        the lower control arm

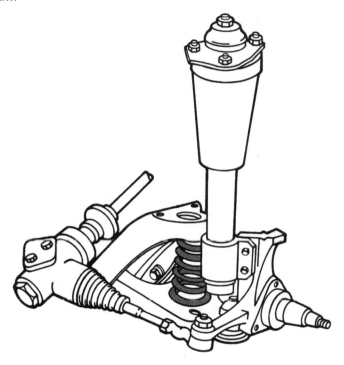

11. Leaf springs are not used on a conventional inde-   11. _____
     pendent front suspension. True or False?

12. Technician A says the conventional independent front   12. _____
     suspension spring is sometimes located between the
     upper control arm and the body. Technician B says
     the conventional independent front suspension spring
     is sometimes located between the lower control arm
     and the body. Who is right?
   (A) A only.
   (B) B only.
   (C) Both A and B.
   (D) Neither A nor B.

13. Torsion bars may be connected to the_____.   13. _____
   (A) upper control arm
   (B) lower control arm
   (C) Both A and B.
   (D) Neither A nor B.

14. Transverse torsion bars are seldom used. True or   14. _____
     False?

Name _____

15. Identify the indicated components in the conventional independent front suspension system shown below.

(A) _____   (D) _____

(B) _____   (E) _____

(C) _____

16. What are two reasons for using solid front axles on some vehicles?

_____

_____

_____

_____

17. Some older trucks may have _____ instead of ball joints. The disadvantage of these devices is that they are unable to adapt to any changes in suspension _____.

17. _____

_____

18. A non-driving solid axle would be used on a(n) _____-wheel drive vehicle.

18. _____

19. Technician A says some solid front axles use coil springs. Technician B says some solid front axles use leaf springs. Who is right?
(A) A only.
(B) B only.
(C) Both A and B.
(D) Neither A nor B.

19. _____

20. The lower ball joint is the load carrying joint on all the following suspensions *except:*
(A) MacPherson strut with the spring around strut assembly.
(B) MacPherson strut with a separate spring.
(C) conventional suspension with the spring on the lower control arm.
(D) conventional suspension with a torsion bar on the lower control arm.

20. _____

Name_____

Date _____ Instructor_____

Score _____ Textbook pages 103–126

Chapter 6

Front Suspension System Service

After studying this chapter, you will be able to:
- ❏ Check for loose, worn, bent, and weak front suspension parts.
- ❏ Use a dial indicator to check front suspension part condition.
- ❏ Check for leaking shock absorbers and strut cartridges.
- ❏ Check sagging springs and/or vehicle ride height.
- ❏ Replace shock absorbers and strut cartridges.
- ❏ Replace ball joints.
- ❏ Replace control arms and control arm bushings.
- ❏ Replace strut rods and strut rod bushings.
- ❏ Replace MacPherson strut suspension system coil springs.
- ❏ Replace conventional suspension coil springs.
- ❏ Replace conventional suspension system torsion bars.
- ❏ Explain how to replace kingpins.

1. Often the only sign of a steering and suspension problem is _____ wear.

1. _____

2. Which suspension parts should be checked whenever a vehicle is brought in for suspension and steering service?

_____

3. Before removing any suspension part, what should the technician determine?

_____

_____

4. Some suspension parts have factory _____ that can be mistaken for damage.

4. _____

5. What do shiny spots on springs or other parts indicate?

_____

_____

Name _____

6. When the method shown in the following illustration is used to check a ball joint, the spring must be between the frame or body and the _____ control arm.

6. _____

Rock wheel in and out

Jack stand

❑   Match the direction of front wheel looseness with the components that may be causing the problem.

7. Top-to-bottom looseness.

(A) Wheel bearings.

7. _____

8. Side-to-side looseness.

(B) Suspension parts.

8. _____

9. Looseness in all directions.

(C) Steering parts.

9. _____

10. The vehicle can be bounced by hand to check _____ _____ condition.

10. _____

11. Technician A says tire pressure will not affect ride height. Technician B says ride height problems are always caused by sagging front springs. Who is right?
    (A) A only.
    (B) B only.
    (C) Both A and B.
    (D) Neither A nor B.

11. _____

12. What types of checks are made with a dial indicator?

_____

_____

13. Torsion bars can be _____ to correct ride height.

13. _____

14. When is it OK to weld a cracked suspension part?

14. _____

15. Some ball joints and control arms are only available as a(n) _____.

15. _____

Name _____

16. The step shown in the illustration below must be
performed when the MacPherson strut has a(n) _____.
(A) separate spring
(B) replaceable cartridge
(C) separate shock absorber
(D) Any of the above.

16. _____

Spanner wrench

Strut
assembly

Vise

Holding fixture

17. Which of the following MacPherson strut reassembly
steps should be taken *last*?
(A) Remove the spring compressor from the spring.
(B) Tighten the piston rod retaining nut.
(C) Install the new strut cartridge assembly through
the spring.
(D) Compare old and new strut cartridge
assemblies.

17. _____

18. After MacPherson struts have been replaced, what must be done before the vehicle is given back to the owner?

_____

_____

19. To remove a conventional shock absorber, which of
the following parts must be removed?
(A) Control arm.
(B) Coil spring.
(C) Torsion bar.
(D) None of the above.

19. _____

20. Before removing the ball joint stud nut, what must you always make sure of?

_____

_____

21. To remove most ball joint studs, you must first break
the _____.

21. _____

Name _____

❑   Match the following tools with the type of ball joint they are used to remove.

22. Chisel.   (A) Riveted.   22. _____

23. Drill.   (B) Bolted.   23. _____

24. Special socket.   (C) Pressed.   24. _____

25. Hydraulic press.   (D) Threaded.   25. _____

26. C-clamp.   26. _____

27. Conventional socket and/or wrench.   27. _____

28. A polished spot on the tapered section of a ball joint   28. _____
    stud may indicate a poor fit between the ball joint
    stud and the _____.
    (A) control arm
    (B) steering knuckle
    (C) ball joint sliding surface
    (D) ball joint seal

29. To replace a control arm bushing, what must usually   29. _____
    be done *first?*
    (A) Remove the control arm from the vehicle.
    (B) Chisel the bushing out of the control arm.
    (C) Inspect the control arm for cracks or other
         damage.
    (D) Check that the new and old bushings match.

30. If a strut rod has threaded nuts on both sides of the   30. _____
    bushing, the rod is used to adjust _____.

31. Technician A says the front suspension must be disas-   31. _____
    sembled to remove a stabilizer bar. Technician B says
    the front suspension must be realigned after stabilizer
    bar replacement. Who is right?
    (A) A only.
    (B) B only.
    (C) Both A and B.
    (D) Neither A nor B.

32. The most common kind of MacPherson strut must be   32. _____
    _____ to replace its spring.

33. Torsion bars may not be _____ between each side of   33. _____
    the vehicle.

34. New kingpin bushings must be _____ for a proper fit.   34. _____

35. Dual kingpin suspensions are being discussed.   35. _____
    Technician A says the upper kingpin cover or tapered
    roller bearing must be removed to eliminate spring
    tension. Technician B says the upper kingpin is
    screwed into the axle. Who is right?
    (A) A only.
    (B) B only.
    (C) Both A and B.
    (D) Neither A nor B.

Name_____

Date _____ Instructor_____

Score _____ Textbook pages 127–146

Chapter 7
Rear Suspension Systems

After studying this chapter, you will be able to:
- ❑ Explain the operation of solid non-driving rear axle suspensions.
- ❑ Explain the operation of solid driving rear axle suspensions.
- ❑ Identify the components of solid rear axle suspensions.
- ❑ Explain the operation of independent non-driving rear axle suspensions.
- ❑ Explain the operation of independent driving rear axle suspensions.
- ❑ Identify the components of independent rear axle suspensions.
- ❑ Identify the components of air-adjustable rear suspensions.

1. The rear suspension causes _____ (more or fewer) handling and tire problems than the front suspension.

2. Name the three types of modern rear suspensions.

3. A non-driving rear axle is used on vehicles with _____-wheel drive. These axles are usually made by forming a single piece of steel into a(n) _____ or _____.

4. To reduce side-to-side and front-to-back movement, the solid rear axle uses both _____ _____ and _____ _____.

5. Most non-driving solid rear axles have control arms that are welded to the _____ and connected to the _____ through bushings.

1. _____

3. _____
   _____
   _____

4. _____
   _____

5. _____
   _____

Name _____

6. Explain the difference between leading and trailing arms as used on solid rear axles.

_____

_____

_____

_____

7. MacPherson struts and conventional non-driving solid axle suspensions always use _____ springs.

7. _____

8. Driving rear axles always contain drive _____. Power is delivered to the axle through a drive _____.

8. _____

_____

9. The advantage of a solid rear driving axle is its _____. The main disadvantage of a solid rear driving axle is extra _____.

9. _____

_____

10. Proper driveline angle is necessary to reduce _____ during acceleration.

10. _____

11. Why are driving axle suspensions designed to place the shortest control arms above the differential?

_____

_____

_____

12. Which of the following vehicles is *most* likely to have leaf springs on the rear suspension?
    (A) Pickup truck.
    (B) Mid-size automobile.
    (C) Sports car.
    (D) None of the above.

12. _____

13. Technician A says the axle tube is always installed over the leaf spring. Technician B says the axle tube is always installed under the leaf spring. Who is right?
    (A) A only.
    (B) B only.
    (C) Both A and B.
    (D) Neither A nor B.

13. _____

14. _____-bolts are used to hold the axle to the leaf spring.

14. _____

15. Pads between the spring leaves reduce _____.

15. _____

16. Leaf spring suspensions do not require control arms, but most use a(n) _____ _____ or _____ _____ to reduce side-to-side movement.

16. _____

_____

Name _____

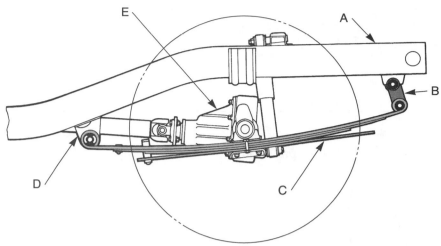

17. Identify the indicated components in the illustration above.

    (A) _____   (D) _____

    (B) _____   (E) _____

    (C) _____

18. On which of the following rear suspension systems is   18. _____
    correct driveline angle the most important?
    (A) Non-driving axle with coil springs.
    (B) Driving axle with longitudinal leaf springs.
    (C) Driving axle with coil springs.
    (D) Non-driving axle with MacPherson struts.

19. Identify the indicated components in the illustration below.

    (A) _____   (D) _____

    (B) _____   (E) _____

    (C) _____

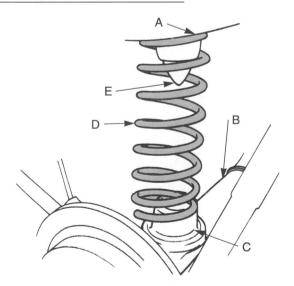

20. Independent non-driving rear axles often resemble   20. _____
    _____ suspensions.

21. Some independent non-driving rear axles use a   21. _____
    MacPherson strut and two lightweight bars that serve
    as the lower _____ _____.

Name _____

22. Many rear suspensions have _____ for adjusting rear
    wheel alignment. The adjustments that can be made
    with these devices are _____ and _____.

22. _____

_____

_____

23. How is a transverse leaf spring mounted?

_____

_____

24. Rear suspension torsion bars have no provision for
    _____ _____ adjustment.

24. _____

25. Which of the following suspension types is *not* used
    on a driving independent rear axle?
    (A) Transverse leaf spring.
    (B) Longitudinal leaf spring.
    (C) Coil spring.
    (D) MacPherson strut.

25. _____

26. A semi-independent rear axle has a connecting bar
    that _____ when one wheel strikes a road irregularity.

26. _____

27. What type of non-driving rear suspension is shown in
    the illustration below?
    (A) Solid with MacPherson struts.
    (B) Solid with shock absorbers.
    (C) Independent with shock absorbers.
    (D) Semi-independent with shock absorbers.

27. _____

28. Normal air suspension system air pressures are about
    _____–_____ psi.

28. _____

29. What is the usual reason for installing aftermarket air shock absorbers?

_____

_____

30. A manual fill air suspension system is filled with air
    from a(n) _____.
    (A) external air source
    (B) on-board compressor
    (C) on-board air reservoir
    (D) None of the above.

30. _____

Name_____

Date _____ Instructor_____

Score_____ Textbook pages 147–166

Chapter 8

Rear Suspension System Service

After studying this chapter, you will be able to:
- ❏ Visually check for worn or bent rear suspension parts.
- ❏ Manually check for loose, worn, and weak rear suspension parts.
- ❏ Check condition of shock absorbers, strut cartridges, and springs.
- ❏ Replace solid rear axle suspension components.
- ❏ Replace independent rear axle suspension components.
- ❏ Add helper springs to rear suspensions.
- ❏ Diagnose air shock absorber and control system problems.
- ❏ Replace air shock absorber and control system components.
- ❏ Install air shock absorbers on vehicles not originally equipped.

1. Where are vibrations caused by the rear suspension felt?

_____

_____

2. Rear tire wear may be in the form of _____ wear patterns that cause _____ that varies with speed.

2. _____

_____

3. Why should a technician never heat or bend a suspension part?

_____

_____

4. Technician A says the rear axle of a front-wheel drive vehicle is easier to damage than the rear axle of a rear-wheel drive vehicle. Technician B says incorrect towing often damages the rear axle of a front wheel-drive vehicle. Who is right?
   (A) A only.
   (B) B only.
   (C) Both A and B.
   (D) Neither A nor B.

4. _____

Name _____

5. Non-driving rear axles are much _____ than driving axles.

5. _____

6. Many defective suspension parts can be found by trying to move related parts by _____.

6. _____

7. A bounce test should be performed on all four _____ of the vehicle.

7. _____

8. Common sources of air shock absorber system leaks include damaged _____ _____ or loose _____.

8. _____

_____

9. An on-vehicle compressor does not produce air pressure when a load is added to the vehicle. All the following could be the cause *except:*
   (A) a defective height control valve.
   (B) a shorted compressor motor.
   (C) a defective electrical pressure switch.
   (D) defects in the compressor piston or valves.

9. _____

10. What vehicle trim pieces might have to be removed to gain access to rear strut top mountings? (Name three.)

_____

_____

11. It may be necessary to push down on the rear _____ to gain enough clearance to remove a rear strut from a vehicle.

11. _____

12. The upper stud nut on some shock absorbers can only be reached by opening the _____ or removing the rear _____.

12. _____

_____

13. What must the technician always do *before* removing the shock absorber fasteners on a solid rear axle with coil springs?

_____

14. Some gas filled shock absorbers should be _____ after they are removed, but before they are disposed of.
    (A) fully extended
    (B) fully retracted
    (C) depressurized
    (D) None of the above.

14. _____

15. Technician A says that the tool shown can be used with a hammer to remove rear axle bushings. Technician B says that the tool shown can be used with hand wrenches to remove rear axle bushings. Who is right?
    (A) A only.
    (B) B only.
    (C) Both A and B.
    (D) Neither A nor B.

15. _____

Name _____

16. Before removing any rear control arm or link with an adjusting cam, what should the technician do first?

    _____

    _____

17. When parts are replaced on a(n) _____ rear suspen-   17. _____
    sion, the rear suspension often must be realigned.

18. The figure below shows a special puller being used to   18. _____
    remove a rear _____ _____.

Puller

19. When removing a coil spring, the axle or control arm   19. _____
    should be lowered slowly using a _____ _____.

20. Before loosening any leaf spring fastener, make sure   20. _____
    all _____ _____ has been removed. If the axle is
    above the spring, _____ it slightly to allow spring   _____
    clearance. If the axle is below the spring, _____ it
    slightly.   _____

21. A special tool is needed to remove a _____-leaf trans-   21. _____
    verse spring used on a _____-_____ axle.
                                                                    _____

22. To remove a transverse spring, which of the following   22. _____
    rear suspension parts must be removed?
    (A) Track bar.
    (B) Clips and brackets.
    (C) MacPherson struts.
    (D) Axle.

23. A variable-rate helper spring is often called a _____   23. _____
    spring.

24. Never drive a vehicle with air shocks unless there is   24. _____
    at least _____ psi of air pressure into the system.

25. The major difference between replacing air shocks   25. _____
    and replacing standard shocks is that the _____ _____
    must be removed and reinstalled.

26. When adding aftermarket air shock absorbers to a   26. _____
    vehicle, the technician must drill a hole to mount the
    _____ valve.

Name_____

Date _____ Instructor_____

Score _____ Textbook pages 167–202

Chapter 9
Steering Systems

After studying this chapter, you will be able to:
- ❑ Identify and explain the operation and components of steering wheels, columns, and related parts.
- ❑ Explain the operation of conventional steering systems.
- ❑ Identify the components of conventional steering systems.
- ❑ Explain the operation of rack-and-pinion steering systems.
- ❑ Identify the components of rack-and-pinion steering systems.
- ❑ Explain the operation of power steering systems.
- ❑ Identify the components of power steering systems.
- ❑ Identify the major types of power steering systems.
- ❑ Explain the operation of four-wheel steering systems.
- ❑ Identify the components of four-wheel steering systems.

1. The primary purpose of the steering system is to allow the driver to _____ the vehicle.

1. _____

2. To reduce tire _____, the steering system should keep the proper angle between the tires and the road.

2. _____

3. All steering systems contain the following parts *except:*
   (A) steering wheel.
   (B) ball sockets.
   (C) rack and pinion.
   (D) steering arms.

3. _____

4. Steering wheel _____ affects turning effort.

4. _____

5. Air bag inflation is often called _____.

5. _____

6. Air bags are triggered by _____ sensors that communicate with the air bag _____ module. The module then sends current to the air bag _____, which ignites a(n) _____ substance in the bag.

6. _____

_____

_____

_____

Name _____

7. The electrical connection to the steering wheel–mounted air bag is provided by a(n) _____.

7. _____

8. When the steering wheel is a tilt type, the upper section of the steering column has a(n) _____ joint.

8. _____

9. Explain the job of the steering arm.

_____

_____

_____

10. What is the purpose of steering stops?

_____

_____

_____

11. The ball sockets used to connect the steering linkage to the steering knuckle are called _____ _____ _____.

11. _____

12. Define *steering ratio*.

_____

_____

_____

13. Rack-and-pinion steering gear ratio is determined by the:
    (A) number of teeth on the rack and on the pinion.
    (B) length of the rack and the number of rack teeth.
    (C) size of the pinion and the number of pinion teeth.
    (D) position of the pinion in relation to the rack.

14. Identify the components in the illustration below.

    (A) _____   (D) _____

    (B) _____   (E) _____

    (C) _____   (F) _____

15. Toe is adjusted by changing the length of the _____ _____ assembly.

19. _____

Name _____

16. Identify the components in the illustration below.

(A) _____   (E) _____

(B) _____   (F) _____

(C) _____   (G) _____

(D) _____

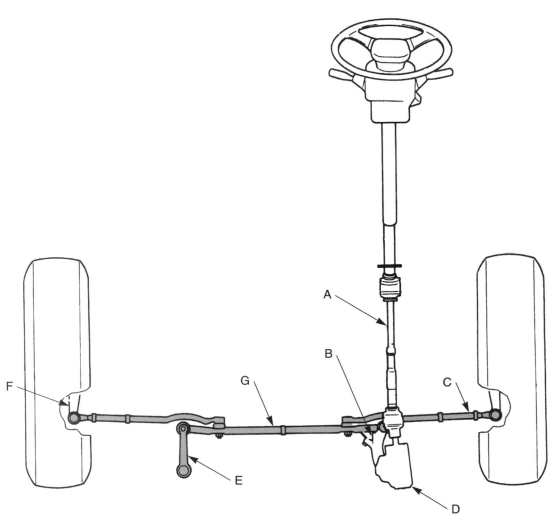

17. Most conventional steering gearboxes have ____ adjusting devices.

17. _____

18. Technician A says variable-ratio steering is used on rack-and-pinion gearboxes. Technician B says variable-ratio steering makes parking maneuvers easier. Who is right?
    (A) A only.
    (B) B only.
    (C) Both A and B.
    (D) Neither A nor B.

18. _____

Name _____

19. Identify the components in the illustration shown below.

(A) _____

(B) _____

(C) _____

(D) _____

(E) _____

(F) _____

(G) _____

☐   Match the following vehicles with the type of conventional steering gearbox they are most likely equipped with.

20. Asian vehicles.   (A)   Recirculating ball.   20. _____

21. Modern domestic cars.   (B)   Worm-and-roller.   21. _____

22. Modern domestic trucks.   (C)   Worm-and-follower.   22. _____

23. Older European vehicles.   23. _____

24. Older Jeeps.   24. _____

25. The most common type of power steering pump   25. _____
    contains all the following *except:*
    (A)   metal vanes.
    (B)   flow control valve.
    (C)   pressure control valve.
    (D)   temperature control valve.

26. The power steering flow regulator allows maximum   26. _____
    flow at _____ speeds.

27. Which of the following is a high-pressure power   27. _____
    steering hose?
    (A)   The hose from the power steering pump to the
          gearbox.
    (B)   The hose from the gearbox to the oil cooler.
    (C)   The hose from the oil cooler to the reservoir.
    (D)   None of the above.

28. Power steering coolers transfer heat from the fluid to   28. _____
    the _____.

Name _____

29. Most power rack-and-pinion and conventional steering gears use a(n) _____ valve to control fluid flow inside of the gear.

29. _____

30. The following illustration shows a rack-and-pinion power steering gear during what steering situation?
    (A) Driving straight ahead.
    (B) Making a right turn.
    (C) Making a left turn.
    (D) Cannot tell from this illustration.

30. _____

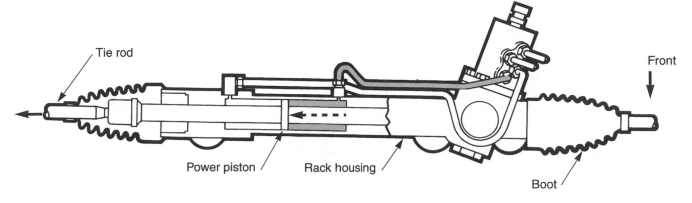

31. An electromechanical four-wheel steering system is the only type of power steering system that does *not* use _____ _____.

31. _____

Name_____

Date _____ Instructor_____

Score _____ Textbook pages 203–224

Chapter 10

Steering Linkage and Manual Steering Gear Service

After studying this chapter, you will be able to:
- ❏ Check for defects in the steering wheel, shaft, and column.
- ❏ Visually check for worn or loose steering linkage.
- ❏ Visually check for bent steering linkage.
- ❏ Manually check for loose steering linkage parts.
- ❏ Disarm an air bag system.
- ❏ Replace steering wheels.
- ❏ Replace steering wheel–mounted air bags.
- ❏ Replace steering columns and related parts.
- ❏ Replace air bag clocksprings.
- ❏ Enable an air bag system.
- ❏ Replace steering system linkage components.
- ❏ Adjust manual steering gears.
- ❏ Replace manual steering gears.

1. Name the five common classes of steering complaints.

_____

_____

_____

2. Name three factors that can affect the life of steering parts.

_____

_____

_____

3. How should you shake the front wheel to determine whether the steering linkage is loose?

_____

Name _____

4. If an inner tie rod on a rack-and-pinion steering gear moves excessively without moving the steering wheel, what is wrong with it?

_____

5. Dirt and grass on the underbody areas are an indication that the vehicle has been

_____.

6. A loose tie rod may be easier to find if the wheel is on the _____.

6. _____

7. Most manual rack-and-pinion gearboxes have a filler plug. True or False?

7. _____

8. What is the first step that should be taken when disarming an air bag?

_____

_____

9. Air bag electrical connectors are often _____ in color.

9. _____

10. List five safety precautions that should be followed when handling disconnected air bags.

_____

_____

_____

_____

11. Before removing a steering wheel, _____ it for proper positioning. This is not necessary if the wheel and shaft have a master _____.

11. _____

_____

12. All the following statements about steering wheel and column repair are true *except:*
   (A) some ignition lock cylinders can be removed without removing the steering wheel.
   (B) the clockspring is the electrical connection for the horn button.
   (C) always check the operation of the steering column parts before reinstalling the steering wheel.
   (D) many electrical connectors for the steering column parts are located under the dashboard.

12. _____

13. The special tool shown in the following illustration is being used to remove a part from the _____.
   (A) upper steering column
   (B) lower steering column
   (C) tilt wheel assembly
   (D) lower steering shaft

13. _____

Retaining clip

Compressor tool

Screwdriver

Name _____

14. Most steering couplings are _____ to one yoke and   14. _____
    _____ to the other.   _____

15. After reinstalling the air bag connectors and fuses but before turning the ignition switch on, what should the tech-
    nician do?

    _____

    _____

16. After any part of the steering linkage is replaced, the   16. _____
    vehicle must be _____.

17. What steering system component is being removed in   17. _____
    the illustration below?
    (A) Outer tie rod.
    (B) Inner tie rod.
    (C) Rack.
    (D) Pinion.

18. Pitman arm removal usually requires the use of a   18. _____
    pickle fork or a special _____.

19. One end of an idler arm is attached to the relay rod   19. _____
    and the other end is attached to the _____.

20. Worn rack-and-pinion gears must generally be _____   20. _____
    or _____.   _____

21. If a manual rack-and-pinion gear is being overhauled,   21. _____
    which of the following parts must be removed first?
    (A) Rack.
    (B) Pinion gear.
    (C) Sliding bearings.
    (D) None of the above.

Name _____

22. After adjusting the sector backlash of a conventional manual steering gearbox, be sure to tighten the _____.

22. _____

23. The following illustration shows a(n) _____ _____ adjusting locknut being loosened in a _____ gearbox.

23. _____

_____

Hammer

Punch

Gear housing

Locknut

Vise

24. If conventional manual steering gearbox adjustments do not reduce play, what should the technician do next?

_____

_____

25. Before removing a steering coupler, _____ each side for reassembly.

25. _____

26. When installing a conventional gearbox, which of the following steps should be taken *last*?
    (A) Install the gearbox-to-frame fasteners.
    (B) Tighten the gearbox-to-frame fasteners.
    (C) Reinstall the pitman arm.
    (D) Install the steering coupler fasteners.

26. _____

27. After placing the manual gearbox on a bench but before beginning disassembly, what should the technician do?

_____

28. Technician A says the worm gear and ball nut are removed from a manual gearbox as an assembly. Technician B says the ball guides should be removed before the worm gear and ball nut are separated. Who is right?
    (A) A only.
    (B) B only.
    (C) Both A and B.
    (D) Neither A nor B.

28. _____

Name _____

29. After disassembling and cleaning the internal parts of   29. _____
    a manual steering gearbox, what should the techni-
    cian do next?
    (A) Reassemble the gearbox using all new parts.
    (B) Reassemble the gearbox using new parts as needed.
    (C) Soak all new parts in the proper gear oil.
    (D) Check the internal parts for wear and damage.

30. After reinstalling the worm gear into the ball nut, an   30. _____
    equal number of _____ must be placed in each
    channel.

Chapter 11

Power Steering and Four-Wheel Steering Service

After studying this chapter, you will be able to:
- ❑ Check for leaks in the power steering system.
- ❑ Check power steering system assist using effort gauges.
- ❑ Check power steering system operation using pressure and flow gauges.
- ❑ Check operation of four-wheel steering systems.
- ❑ Adjust and/or replace power steering pump drive belts.
- ❑ Replace power steering hoses and oil coolers.
- ❑ Replace power steering pumps and steering gears.
- ❑ Bleed power steering systems to remove air.
- ❑ Replace four-wheel steering system components.

1. Define *hard steering* as it applies to a power steering system.

_____

_____

2. Momentary hard steering is called _____.

2. _____

3. Define *power steering oversteer.*

_____

_____

4. The two main power steering maintenance procedures are checking _____ tightness and checking
_____ level. If the system has a(n) _____ _____, it
should be checked for leaks and dirt.

4. _____

_____

_____

Name _____

5. Technician A says the power steering system is the cause of most suspension complaints. Technician B says all other steering and suspension parts should be checked before checking the power steering system. Who is right?
   (A) A only.
   (B) B only.
   (C) Both A and B.
   (D) Neither A nor B.

5. _____

❑ Match the power steering system noise with its *most likely* cause.

6. Screeching.

7. Squealing.

8. Suction.

9. Whining during turns.

10. Whining that varies with engine speed.

(A) Low fluid level.

(B) Worn pump.

(C) Restricted hose.

(D) Loose belt.

6. _____

7. _____

8. _____

9. _____

10. _____

11. Power steering fluid that is very _____ or smells _____ should be replaced with new fluid.

11. _____
_____

12. Power steering hoses should be checked periodically for _____ in the metal lines and _____ of the flexible hoses.

12. _____
_____

13. Swollen power steering hoses should be _____.

13. _____

14. The tension of a power steering _____ belt should be checked periodically. This is not necessary if the belt is a(n) _____ type.

14. _____
_____

15. Check all belts for a(n) _____ inner surface. If the belt driven units can be turned by hand, the belt is too _____.

15. _____
_____

16. When checking the drive belts, also check the _____ for wear and proper alignment.

16. _____

17. All the following statements about checking power steering pressure are true *except:*
   (A) most manufacturers specify a 1000 RPM engine speed for checking.
   (B) the pressure gauge should be able to read at least 2000 psi (13,790 kPa).
   (C) the shutoff valve should be closed for no more than five seconds.
   (D) system pressure should be at least 2000 psi (13,790 kPa).

17. _____

Name _____

18. The tester shown below is used to make which of the
    following power steering system checks?
    (A) Fluid viscosity.
    (B) System pressure.
    (C) System flow.
    (D) Fluid temperature.

18. _____

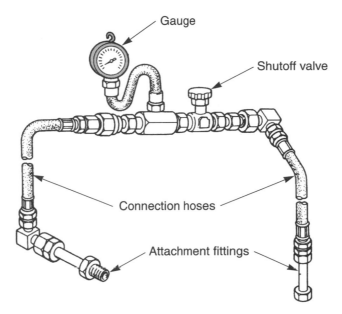

Gauge

Shutoff valve

Connection hoses

Attachment fittings

19. The belt adjustment setup shown below is used with
    a(n) _____ belt.
    (A) V-
    (B) serpentine
    (C) constant-tension
    (D) None of the above.

19. _____

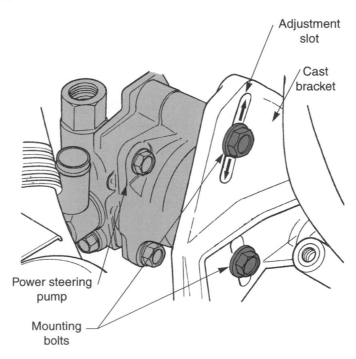

Adjustment
slot

Cast
bracket

Power steering
pump

Mounting
bolts

Name _____

20. Technician A says some power steering pump pulleys can be replaced. Technician B says in some cases, the entire power steering pump must be replaced if the pulley is damaged. Who is right?
   (A) A only.
   (B) B only.
   (C) Both A and B.
   (D) Neither A nor B.

20. _____

21. Always _____ the power steering system after replacing components.

21. _____

22. Technician A says damaged cooler hoses should be replaced. Technician B says damaged cooler lines should be replaced. Who is right?
   (A) A only.
   (B) B only.
   (C) Both A and B.
   (D) Neither A nor B.

22. _____

23. The original fluid can be reused after minor system repairs. True or False?

23. _____

24. There are many minor differences between power steering pumps. True or False?

24. _____

25. Most power steering pumps with the reservoir installed around the pump have a(n) _____ cover. This cover is usually held in place by a(n) _____ _____. If the pump is separate from the reservoir, the pump cover may be attached by _____.

25. _____
    _____
    _____
    _____

26. The following illustration shows the pump vanes being installed in the slots of the pump _____, which is located inside of the _____ ring.

26. _____
    _____

27. Before reinstalling an overhauled power steering pump, make sure the pump shaft _____ freely.

27. _____

28. Whenever overhauling any kind of power steering gear, never reuse old _____.
   (A) gears
   (B) valves
   (C) seals
   (D) None of the above.

28. _____

Name _____

29. On a conventional power steering gear, the power
    piston seals will be installed on which of the
    following components?
    (A) Ball nut and worn assembly.
    (B) Sector gear.
    (C) Rotary control valve.
    (D) Ball guides.

29. _____

30. The control valve of a linkage-type power steering
    system must be removed from the _____ _____ for
    overhaul. If the control valve sticks in its bore, it can
    be lightly _____.

30. _____
    _____

31. Which of the following parts of a linkage-type power
    steering power piston can be replaced?
    (A) All internal parts.
    (B) The outer piston seal.
    (C) The piston rod.
    (D) None of the above.

31. _____

32. All of the following statements about rear steering
    gear service are true *except:*
    (A) some rear steering gear tie rod ends can be
         serviced.
    (B) rear steering gear service is similar to that for a
         front rack and pinion gear.
    (C) the rear steering gear can be overhauled while
         installed on the vehicle.
    (D) removing some rear steering gears requires the
         use of a special lock tool.

32. _____

33. Which of the following power steering bleeding
    procedures should be performed *first*?
    (A) Move the vehicle to avoid scrubbing flat spots
         on the tires.
    (B) If you hear a suction sound, stop the engine
         and add fluid.
    (C) Allow the vehicle to sit until all foam
         disappears.
    (D) Add fluid to the full mark.

33. _____

34. What provides the fluid flow necessary to flush a power steering system?

    _____

35. What step should the technician perform to begin the flushing procedure?

    _____

    _____

Chapter 12

Driveline and Wheel Components

After studying this chapter, you will be able to:
- ❏ Identify types of drive axles and drive shafts.
- ❏ Explain the design and construction of constant velocity flexible joints.
- ❏ Explain the design and construction of cross-and-roller flexible joints.
- ❏ Explain the purpose of antifriction bearings.
- ❏ Identify types of wheel bearings.
- ❏ Match axle types to bearing types.
- ❏ Identify types of hubs and axle flanges.
- ❏ Identify types of wheel rims.
- ❏ Explain rim size specifications.
- ❏ Identify tire designs.
- ❏ Explain tire ratings.
- ❏ Identify wheel fastener designs.

1. Identify the parts in the following illustration.

   (A) _____

   (B) _____

   (C) _____

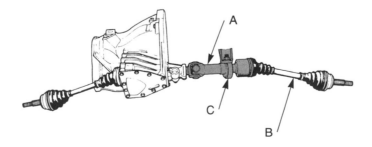

Name _____

2. Identify the parts in the illustration below.

(A) _____   (C) _____

(B) _____   (D) _____

3. Does the axle design in the illustration above use a C-lock to hold the axle shaft in place?

3. _____

4. Slip yokes are used on _____-wheel drive vehicles.

4. _____

5. The purpose of all types of driveline flexible joints is to allow the driveline _____ to change.
   (A) length
   (B) angle
   (C) speed
   (D) load

5. _____

6. Rzeppa and tripod joints are both _____ joints. To protect them and retain their lubricant, they are always covered with flexible _____.

6. _____

_____

7. Why do axles with Rzeppa or tripod joints not use a slip yoke?

_____

_____

_____

8. U-joints are used on drivelines where the _____ between the yokes is relatively small.

8. _____

9. The purpose of wheel bearings is to provide a low _____ connection between the wheels and the vehicle.

9. _____

10. Technician A says bearing preload tends to push the bearing parts together. Technician B says bearing preload tends to cause premature bearing wear. Who is right?
   (A) A only.
   (B) B only.
   (C) Both A and B.
   (D) Neither A nor B.

10. _____

Name _____

11. Vehicle weight and centrifugal force produce a _____ load on the bearing. This load is at a _____ angle to the bearing and shaft.

11. _____

_____

12. Bearing loads that occur when a vehicle is turned are called _____ loads. This load is _____ to the shaft.

12. _____

_____

❏ Match the bearing description below with the bearing type at right. Some descriptions apply to more than one type of bearing.

13. Have adjustable preload.

(A) Ball bearing.

13. _____

14. Used on non-driving front axles.

(B) Roller bearing.

14. _____

15. All elements in a single sealed unit.

(C) Tapered roller bearing.

15. _____

16. Usually used in sets of two.

16. _____

17. Used on rear axles of rear-wheel drive vehicles.

17. _____

18. Used on front axles of some front-wheel drive vehicles.

18. _____

19. _____

19. Inner race and rolling elements in a single unit.

20. _____

20. The axle shaft may be the inner race.

21. Of the three main types of wheel bearings, which is the *least* likely to be greased for the life of the bearing?

_____

22. Technician A says the job of a bearing seal is to keep dirt out of the bearing. Technician B says the job of a bearing seal is to keep lubricant in the bearing. Who is right?
(A) A only.
(B) B only.
(C) Both A and B.
(D) Neither A nor B.

22. _____

23. The wheel hub is used as the mounting surface for all of the following *except:*
(A) the rim and tire.
(B) the brake drum or rotor.
(C) the bearing races.
(D) the spindle.

23. _____

24. On a solid rear axle, the wheel and tire are often connected to the axle shaft through an axle _____ that is formed or _____ onto the axle shaft.

24. _____

_____

25. Many wheel rims are made of stamped _____. After stamping, the individual wheel parts are _____ into a single unit. Other wheel materials include aluminum, aluminum-magnesium _____, and composites of _____ and _____.

25. _____

_____

_____

_____

_____

26. The three most common rim measurements are _____, _____, and _____.

26. _____

_____

_____

Name _____

27. The major outer parts of a tire are the _____ and
    _____.

27. _____

    _____

28. The inner parts of a tire are plies and _____. Plies are
    layers of tire _____.

28. _____

    _____

29. All modern tires are _____ tires. Older tires were
    called _____ tires.

29. _____

    _____

30. A letter W at the end of the rating molded into the
    sidewall of a tire indicates which of the following?
    (A) The tire is rated for high speed driving.
    (B) The tire has a low aspect ratio.
    (C) The tire section width is very large.
    (D) The tire is a truck tire.

30. _____

31. Does a tire with a DOT temperature rating of C have
    more or less heat resistance than a tire with a temper-
    ature rating of A?

31. _____

32. If the DOT tread wear rating of a tire is 450, how much longer should it last than a tire rated at 150?

    _____

33. How are most wheel studs attached to the wheel hub or axle flange?

    _____

    _____

34. The matching _____ in the wheel rim and lug nut help
    to _____ the wheel when the lug nuts are tightened.

34. _____

    _____

35. On all but steel wheels, it is important that the wheels
    be tightened to a specific _____.

35. _____

Chapter 13

Driveline and Wheel Service

After studying this chapter, you will be able to:
- ❑ Check for drive axle and drive shaft defects.
- ❑ Check for flexible joint defects.
- ❑ Check for wheel bearing defects.
- ❑ Check for rim and tire defects.
- ❑ Replace CV axle shafts and CV joints.
- ❑ Replace solid axles.
- ❑ Replace drive shafts and U-joints.
- ❑ Repack tapered wheel bearings.
- ❑ Replace bearings on front and rear drive axles.
- ❑ Replace rims and tires.
- ❑ Repair tire leaks.
- ❑ Replace wheel fasteners.

1. Most rear axle vibrations are felt in the vehicle's _____.

1. _____

2. A feeling that the steering wheel is moving right and left is called _____. It is usually caused by a bad _____.

2. _____

_____

3. Whines and roaring noises are often caused by defects in the _____ or _____.

3. _____

_____

4. Why should a technician *never* ignore a torn CV boot?

_____

_____

_____

Name _____

5. A worn two-piece drive shaft center support can cause the drive shaft to rub against the vehicle's _____.

5. _____

6. All of the following are methods of adjusting the driveline angle of a rear-wheel drive vehicle *except:*
   (A) adding or removing shims at the rear leaf springs.
   (B) adding or removing shims at the rear transmission mount.
   (C) adding or removing shims at the differential yoke.
   (D) turning adjusting cams on the rear axle assembly.

6. _____

7. The tool shown in the following illustration is used to check _____ angles. It is called a(n) _____.

7. _____

_____

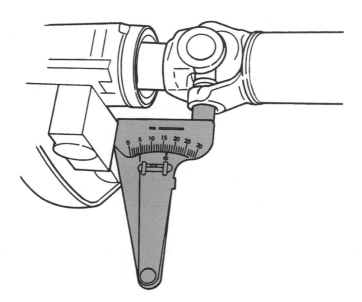

8. The hose clamps shown in the following illustration are used as part of a procedure to _____ a drive shaft.

8. _____

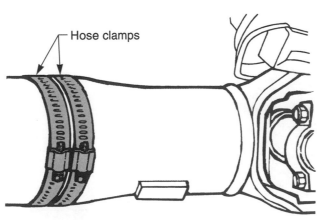

Hose clamps

9. To check for a damaged bearing, rotate the wheel off the ground and check for _____ and _____. Also check for _____ by shaking the wheel.

9. _____

_____

_____

Name _____

10. If a wheel rim has excessive runout, what should be   10. _____
    done to correct the problem?
    (A) Replace the rim.
    (B) Straighten the rim using a large adjustable
        wrench.
    (C) Heat and hammer the rim to straighten it.
    (D) Make sure the heaviest part of the tire is oppo-
        site the rim.

11. What should the technician do to check for tire pulling?

    _____

    _____

12. If the procedure in Question 11 is performed, what result would indicate a defective tire?

    _____

13. If the information gathered in Questions 11 and 12 indicates that a tire is defective, what tire would most likely
    be defective?

    _____

    _____

14. Before checking tire balance, check the tire for _____.   14. _____
    Before spinning a tire on any type of balance
    machine, _____ should be removed from the tire   _____
    tread.

15. What is the usual cause of wheel stud damage?

    _____

    _____

16. Why should a technician always check the service manual before removing a CV axle shaft retaining nut?

    _____

    _____

17. A special puller may be needed to remove the   17. _____
    CV axle from the _____.
    (A) transaxle
    (B) wheel hub
    (C) control arm
    (D) Both A and B.

Name _____

18. The illustration below shows a special tool being used to: 18. _____
    (A) remove a broken wheel stud.
    (B) install a replacement wheel stud.
    (C) remove a CV axle from a hub.
    (D) install a CV axle in a hub.

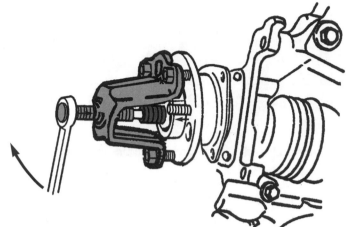

19. Any CV joint lubricant not used during assembly of the CV joint should be _____.   19. _____
    (A) placed in the boot before the clamps are installed
    (B) used to lubricate the other CV joint
    (C) discarded
    (D) saved for use on wheel bearings

❏   Match the type of solid rear axle fastener at right with the parts that must be removed to service it.

20. Backing plate fasteners.   (A) Retainer plate.   20. _____

21. Differential cover.   (B) C-lock.   21. _____

22. Inner housing seal.   22. _____

23. Differential spider gear shaft.   23. _____

24. Bearing O-ring.   24. _____

25. To remove a drive shaft, slide the shaft forward until the _____ _____ clears the differential. Then the drive shaft can be slid from the _____.   25. _____
    _____

26. U-joint bearing caps can be pressed from the yoke by using two large _____ and a bench _____.   26. _____
    _____

27. Most front wheel tapered roller bearings are held in place with an adjusting nut that is kept from rotating by a(n) _____ _____.   27. _____

Name _____

28. In the illustration below, the technician is checking a tapered roller bearing for _____.

28. _____

Inner race

29. To prevent damage, a new bearing race should be installed using a(n) _____ _____.

29. _____

30. In the illustration below, the technician is _____ a tapered roller bearing by hand.

30. _____

31. A new _____ should be used whenever the bearings are repacked.

31. _____

32. Why should the technician tighten the wheel bearing-adjusting nut to 100 ft-lb (135.5 N•m) before adjusting the bearings?

_____

_____

33. All the following statements about wheel bearings are true *except:*
   (A) lubricant stains are not a cause for bearing replacement.
   (B) preload can be adjusted on ball and tapered roller bearings.
   (C) shock loads cause brinelling.
   (D) straight roller bearings are replaced when they become too loose.

33. _____

34. Some front-wheel drive bearings are _____ into the axle hub. Other front wheel drive bearings are held by a(n) _____ _____.

34. _____

_____

Name _____

35. Solid axle bearing collars are being discussed. Technician A says a bearing collar is removed by pressing it from the shaft. Technician B says a bearing collar is installed by pressing it onto the shaft. Who is right?
    (A) A only.
    (B) B only.
    (C) Both A and B.
    (D) Neither A nor B.

35. _____

36. If a rear axle shaft shows signs of wear where the _____ _____ or _____ rides, the shaft should be replaced.

36. _____
    _____

37. A leak in a(n) _____ rim can be fixed by careful brazing.

37. _____

38. Tire rotating involves moving the tire to a different _____.

38. _____

39. Most tire manufacturers recommend replacing the _____ _____ when a tire is replaced.

39. _____

40. Adding too much _____ _____ can cause a tire to explode.

40. _____

41. Under what circumstances should a sidewall leak be repaired?

    _____
    _____

42. Some manufacturers recommend against repairing tires by installing a(n) _____ without dismounting the tire.

42. _____

43. If a tire is removed from the rim, it must be _____.

43. _____

44. What method can be used to remove most damaged studs?

    _____
    _____

45. A new stud can be drawn into the hub using one of the lug nuts and several _____.

45. _____

Chapter 14

Electronic Suspension and Steering Systems

After studying this chapter, you will be able to:
- ❑ Identify the components of electronic suspension systems.
- ❑ Explain the operation of electronic suspension systems.
- ❑ Identify types of electronic suspension systems.
- ❑ Explain the operation of electronic steering systems.
- ❑ Identify the components of electronic steering systems.

1. Electronic suspension systems that control ride quality and ride height are operated by _____ pressure. Electronic suspension systems that affect only ride quality control the shock absorber _____ system.

1. _____

_____

2. A height sensor converts the relative position of the body and axle to an electrical signal by using _____ or _____ to affect current flow through the sensor.

2. _____

_____

3. An accelerometer measures the rate of vehicle _____ or _____.

3. _____

_____

4. Switches are devices that can be either _____ or _____.

4. _____

_____

5. What is the purpose of the suspension service switch?

_____

_____

6. On some vehicles, there is no separate electronic suspension control module. Why?

_____

_____

Name _____

7. Most electronic suspension air compressors are single _____ types with inlet and outlet _____ _____.

7. _____

_____

8. The pressure relief valve prevents system air pressure from becoming too _____.

8. _____

9. A few compressors use a(n) _____ relay, which is controlled by the module and operates the compressor motor.

9. _____

10. What is the purpose of desiccant?

_____

_____

11. Some air suspension control dryers contain a(n) _____ _____ to maintain pressure in the system.

11. _____

12. Which of the following parts is *not* used with the rear suspension shown below?
   (A) Compressor.
   (B) Shock absorber.
   (C) Control module.
   (D) Input sensors.

12. _____

13. Hydraulic flow control solenoids are pulsed on and off. The percentage of time the solenoids are on is called the _____ _____.

13. _____

14. What are the two purposes of electronic suspension indicator lights?

_____

_____

15. Most electronic suspension warning lights will come on when the engine is _____.

15. _____

16. Each of the following is common to all electronic suspension systems *except:*
   (A) height sensor.
   (B) brake pressure switch.
   (C) suspension service switch.
   (D) indicator lights.

16. _____

Name _____

17. Ride height adjustment devices are air _____ or air
    _____ _____.

17. _____

    _____

18. Air suspensions vary pressure in relation to vehicle
    _____ or _____.

18. _____

    _____

19. A height-sensitive electronic suspension control
    system responds to changes in vehicle _____.
    (A) load
    (B) speed
    (C) cornering
    (D) braking

19. _____

20. Identify the components in the illustration below.

    (A) _____

    (C) _____

    (B) _____

    (D) _____

21. The combination electronic suspension control has
    _____ damped components and _____ springs.

21. _____

    _____

22. All electronic steering control systems provide
    maximum power assist at _____ speeds and reduce
    assist at _____ speeds.

22. _____

    _____

23. Electronic steering control systems operate by monitoring two things:

    _____

    _____

24. Where can the vehicle speed sensor be installed?

    _____

    _____

25. The vehicle speed sensor has two main components.
    The _____ _____ rotates with the output shaft and the
    _____ generates a signal, which is sent to the control
    module.

25. _____

    _____

Name _____

❑   Match the parts of an optical steering wheel rotation sensor with their function.

26. Photo cell.   (A)   Breaks the light beam.   26. _____

27. Shutter assembly.   (B)   Creates a magnetic field.   27. _____

28. Photo diode.   (C)   Creates a light signal.   28. _____

                                   (D)   Receives a light signal.

29. How many output devices do electronic steering control systems have?   29. _____

❑   Match the electronic steering control device to its function.

30. Flow control solenoid.   (A)   Prevents wheel kickback.   30. _____

31. Pressure control solenoid.   (B)   Diverts fluid to the reservoir.   31. _____

32. Inlet hose check valve.   (C)   Controls steering gear pressure.   32. _____

33. Electromagnet.   (D)   Reduces pump speed.   33. _____

                                   (E)   Increases steering gear valve resistance.

34. Technician A says an electromagnetic steering wheel   34. _____
    rotation sensor creates ac voltage. Technician B says
    the rotation sensor signal tells the control module
    exactly where the wheel is pointing. Who is right?
    (A)   A only.
    (B)   B only.
    (C)   Both A and B.
    (D)   Neither A nor B.

35. An electronic steering control system uses an electro-   35. _____
    magnetic coil in the steering gear control valve. What
    does energizing the coil accomplish?
    (A)   Sends a signal to the control module.
    (B)   Cancels the steering wheel rotation sensor
          input.
    (C)   Reduces pressure reaching the control valve.
    (D)   Increases the resistance between the control
          valve sections.

Name_____

Date _____ Instructor_____

Score_____ Textbook pages 317–342

Chapter 15

Electronic Suspension and Steering Service

After studying this chapter, you will be able to:
- ❑ Retrieve trouble codes.
- ❑ Make visual checks for electronic suspension and steering problems.
- ❑ Use scan tools to check electronic suspension and steering systems.
- ❑ Use schematics to help isolate electronic suspension and steering system problems.
- ❑ Check for incorrect electronic suspension system operation.
- ❑ Test electronic suspension system components.
- ❑ Check for incorrect electronic steering system operation.
- ❑ Test electronic steering system components.
- ❑ Replace electronic suspension system components.
- ❑ Replace electronic steering system components.

1. Air leaks are usually accompanied by body _____.

1. _____

2. On most electronic suspension systems, the system warning light will come on during which of the following situations (more than one choice may be used)?
   (A) Engine start up.
   (B) Body rises.
   (C) Body drops.
   (D) System defect occurs.

2. _____

3. The simplest test of an electronic suspension system is to _____

_____.

4. When the test referred to in Question 3 is performed, what should happen?

_____

_____

Name _____

5. If a vehicle has an OBD II computer, how are trouble codes retrieved?

_____

_____

What could happen if another method of code retrieval is used on an OBD II system?

_____

_____

6. The following illustration shows a multimeter being used to _____.
   (A) reprogram the control module
   (B) check ride height adjustment
   (C) verify warning light operation
   (D) retrieve trouble codes

6. _____

Data link connector

Analog voltmeter

Ground

7. On older (OBD I) systems, trouble codes can be retrieved by _____ a terminal of the diagnostic connector. On most vehicles, this will cause a dashboard light to _____.

7. _____

_____

8. Name four obvious electrical problems that can cause electronic suspension system malfunctions.

_____

_____

_____

_____

9. Normal charging voltage should be over _____ volts but not more than _____ volts.

9. _____

_____

10. To check a height sensor, disconnect and manually move the _____ _____ with the ignition in the *on* position. If this does not cause the system to vary vehicle _____, a defect is present.

10. _____

_____

11. Most speed sensors can be tested with multimeters or a(n) _____ tool.

11. _____

Name _____

12. All the devices that use a certain speed sensor as input are malfunctioning. What is the *most* likely problem?
  (A) Each of the devices is defective.
  (B) One device is malfunctioning and affecting the others.
  (C) The speed sensor is defective.
  (D) Cannot tell from the information given.

12. _____

13. Pushing down on the rear bumper of a running vehicle with an electronic suspension system should cause the compressor to _____.
  (A) start
  (B) stop
  (C) reverse
  (D) Cannot tell from the information given.

13. _____

14. _____ air leaks are usually easy to find.

14. _____

15. If the compressor does not operate when it is bypassed with _____ _____, it is defective.

15. _____

16. If system air pressure drops to zero when the engine is turned off, the system is operating properly. True or False?

16. _____

17. Technician A says some solenoids can be tested with jumper wires. Technician B says some solenoids can be checked with an ohmmeter. Who is right?
  (A) A only.
  (B) B only.
  (C) Both A and B.
  (D) Neither A nor B.

17. _____

18. There are two methods for adjusting height sensors. They are _____ and _____ _____.

18. _____
_____

19. The control module can be ruined by _____ electricity.

19. _____

20. Care must be taken when installing accelerometers, since they are sensitive to changes in _____.
  (A) temperature
  (B) position
  (C) static electricity
  (D) light

20. _____

21. Many air spring solenoids are installed on the air spring in a manner similar to the way a(n) _____ _____ is installed.

21. _____

22. Before removing an air spring solenoid, make sure all _____ _____ has been removed from the system.

22. _____

Name _____

23. A vehicle with an electronic steering control system
has too much power steering assist at high speeds.
Steering assist at low speeds is normal. Which of the
following could *not* be a cause of this condition?
   (A) Worn out power steering pump.
   (B) Incorrect solenoid duty cycle.
   (C) Shorted control module.
   (D) Defective speed sensor.

23. _____

24. The power steering control solenoid's _____ _____
can be checked with a scan tool. Other control solenoids can be tested with a(n) _____.

24. _____

    _____

25. After a power steering pump control solenoid has
been replaced, the system must be _____.

25. _____

Name_____

Date _____ Instructor_____

Score _____ Textbook pages 343–360

Chapter 16
Wheel Alignment Principles

After studying this chapter, you will be able to:
- ❑ Explain the purpose of two-wheel alignment.
- ❑ Explain the purpose of four-wheel alignment.
- ❑ Identify and explain caster angle, camber angle, toe, and other wheel alignment angles.
- ❑ Identify adjustable and nonadjustable wheel alignment angles.
- ❑ Identify outside forces that can affect alignment.
- ❑ Describe vehicle alignment adjustment devices.
- ❑ Explain how suspension, steering, tire, and frame defects can affect alignment.

1. Wheel alignment is important to maintain proper vehicle _____ and reduce _____ _____.

1. _____

_____

2. Moving various _____ and _____ components changes the wheel alignment.

2. _____

_____

❑ Match the vehicle with the type of alignment that it is most likely to require.

3. Rear-wheel drive car with a solid rear axle.

4. Rear-wheel drive car with an independent rear axle.

5. Rear-wheel drive pickup truck with a solid rear axle.

6. Rear-wheel drive SUV with a solid rear axle.

7. Front-wheel drive car with a solid rear axle.

8. Front-wheel drive car with an independent rear axle.

(A) Two-wheel alignment.

(B) Four-wheel alignment.

3. _____

4. _____

5. _____

6. _____

7. _____

8. _____

9. Wheel alignment consists of checking and adjusting a series of interrelated _____.

9. _____

10. 45° and 45 _____ mean the same thing.

10. _____

Name _____

11. All the following statements about wheel alignment angles are true *except:*
   (A) alignment angles set the tire position in relation to the road and the vehicle's body.
   (B) alignment angles set the tire position in relation to the other tires.
   (C) all vehicle alignment angles are adjustable.
   (D) all vehicle alignment angles are interrelated.

11. _____

12. Which of the following front camber angle settings is the most common on modern cars and trucks?
   (A) 1° positive.
   (B) 8° positive.
   (C) 1° negative.
   (D) 7° negative.

12. _____

13. Camber is set so that most of a vehicle's weight passes through the _____ wheel bearing.

13. _____

14. The figure below is an illustration of which of the following?
   (A) Negative caster.
   (B) Positive caster.
   (C) Negative camber.
   (D) Positive camber.

14. _____

MacPherson strut

15. On a conventional suspension, the steering axis is formed by the position of the lower ball joint in relation to the upper _____ _____. On a MacPherson strut suspension, the steering axis is formed by the position of the lower ball joint in relation to the upper _____ _____.

15. _____

   _____

16. The back-and-forth position of the _____ _____ determines caster.

16. _____

17. Caster can be _____.
   (A) positive
   (B) negative
   (C) Either A or B.
   (D) None of the above.

17. _____

Name _____

18. Technician A says the tendency of the wheels to move in a straight line is called tracking. Technician B says the tendency of the wheels to move in a straight line is called recovery. Who is right?
    (A) A only.
    (B) B only.
    (C) Both A and B.
    (D) Neither A nor B.

18. _____

19. Negative caster contributes to recovery from a turn. True or False?

19. _____

20. Technician A says caster has no effect on tire life. Technician B says caster has no effect on pulling. Who is right?
    (A) A only.
    (B) B only.
    (C) Both A and B.
    (D) Neither A nor B.

20. _____

21. Negative caster can cause _____ _____, a condition in which the vehicle tries to steer away from the driver as it travels over road irregularities.

21. _____

22. Caster is not measured on the _____ wheels.

22. _____

23. For maximum tire life, the tires on an axle should be _____ to each other. The alignment angle used to accomplish this is called _____.

23. _____
    _____

24. Included angle is a combination of _____ and _____.

24. _____
    _____

25. All the following statements about toe-out on turns are true *except:*
    (A) during a turn the inner wheel turns in a shorter radius.
    (B) both steering arms angle slightly inward.
    (C) steering arm shape causes toe to remain "in" when the vehicle is turned.
    (D) steering arm shape has no effect on straight-ahead driving.

25. _____

❑   Below is a list of alignment angles. Write the letter **a** on the line next to the angle if it is adjustable; write the letter **n** on the line if the angle in non-adjustable.

26. Caster

26. _____

27. Setback

27. _____

28. Steering axis inclination

28. _____

29. Camber

29. _____

30. Toe

30. _____

31. Toe out on turns

31. _____

32. Steering wheel position

32. _____

Name _____

33. One cause of pulling not caused by vehicle alignment is defective seals in the _____ _____ system. Another cause of pulling not caused by alignment is a tire defect called _____ _____.

33. _____

_____

34. Three conditions that indicate an alignment problem might be caused by a bent frame are:

_____

_____

_____

35. To compensate for road crown, caster and camber may be _____ from side to side.

35. _____

36. Adding a heavy load to a vehicle will affect _____.
    (A) caster
    (B) camber
    (C) toe
    (D) All of the above.

36. _____

37. Turning forces are _____ force and _____. The difference between the intended path of a turn and the actual path is called the _____ angle. This angle increases with vehicle cornering _____.

37. _____

_____

_____

_____

38. The shims in the illustration below are called _____ - _____ tapered shims.

38. _____

_____

Name _____

39. The slot in the illustration below is used to make what   39. _____
    adjustment?
    (A) Front camber.
    (B) Rear camber.
    (C) Front toe.
    (D) Rear toe.

Adjustment slot

Compensator
arm

Trailing arm

40. The bolt of an eccentric cam is usually attached to the   40. _____
    control arm through a(n) _____.   _____

41. Most eccentric bolts move inside of a _____.   41. _____
    (A) circular hole
    (B) square hole
    (C) slot
    (D) Any of the above.

42. Frame straightening can be done by _____.   42. _____
    (A) most alignment shops
    (B) all body shops
    (C) a body shop with the proper equipment
    (D) All of the above.

Name _____

Date _____ Instructor _____

Score _____ Textbook pages 361–390

Chapter 17

Wheel Alignment Procedures

After studying this chapter, you will be able to:
- ❏ Explain the difference between two- and four-wheel alignment.
- ❏ Identify types of alignment equipment.
- ❏ Explain pre-alignment vehicle checks.
- ❏ Describe rack, machine, and vehicle pre-alignment setup.
- ❏ Explain wheel alignment checking procedures.
- ❏ Identify alignment adjustment devices.
- ❏ Explain wheel alignment adjusting procedures.
- ❏ Identify the purpose of post-alignment checks and road testing.
- ❏ Explain why frame straightening must be done by a body shop.

1. All the following situations call for having a vehicle aligned *except:*
   (A) a steering part has been replaced.
   (B) normal wear has occurred.
   (C) the vehicle has been in a collision.
   (D) the vehicle has been in storage since the last alignment.

1. _____

2. The most common type of alignment in the past was the _____-wheel alignment. The most common type of alignment today is the _____-wheel alignment.

2. _____
   _____

3. Three simple alignment checking devices are the _____ gauge, the _____ bar, and _____ _____ plate. These may be useful to check the approximate alignment of _____ cars and trucks.

3. _____
   _____
   _____
   _____
   _____

4. An alignment rack must have _____ plates or it is useless.

4. _____

Name _____

5. All modern alignment machines are operated by a built-in _____. Older machines often used _____ beams.

5. _____

_____

6. The alignment devices installed on the wheel rims are called alignment _____.

6. _____

7. If possible, how should the technician start any vehicle alignment?

_____

8. Before driving the vehicle onto the rack, make sure that the turning plate _____ _____ are in place. Then drive the vehicle onto the rack until the _____ _____ are centered over the turning plates.

8. _____

_____

9. Before performing a wheel alignment, perform all the following steps *except:*
   (A) check tire air pressure.
   (B) make a shake test of the suspension parts.
   (C) turn the trunk suspension switch on.
   (D) check vehicle ride height.

9. _____

10. A vehicle is being aligned. The owner states that the tires were rotated within the last 50 miles. Which of the following statements is true?
   (A) The rear tires will indicate front suspension condition.
   (B) The tire air pressure does not have to be checked.
   (C) It is now impossible to diagnose front end problems from tire condition.
   (D) The vehicle should not be aligned until it has been driven another 1000 miles.

10. _____

11. A vehicle cannot be properly aligned if one tire _____.
   (A) has low air pressure
   (B) has badly worn treads
   (C) is a different size than the other tires
   (D) All of the above.

11. _____

12. Check for obvious wheel _____, especially if the vehicle has obvious collision damage.

12. _____

13. Define *curb weight.*

_____

_____

_____

14. Which of the following alignment steps should be performed *first?*
   (A) Install the alignment heads.
   (B) Calibrate the alignment heads.
   (C) Remove the wheel covers.
   (D) Lower the front wheels.

14. _____

Name _____

15. Before lowering the vehicle onto the turning plates, remove the _____ _____. If the vehicle has power steering, start the engine before _____ the steering wheel.

15. _____

_____

16. Before checking caster, be sure the brake pedal _____ has been installed.

16. _____

17. Steering axis inclination (SAI) is usually checked as part of the _____ checking process.

17. _____

18. If a driver complains of excessive tire squeal on turns, what should the alignment technician check?

_____

19. If a four-wheel alignment is being performed, which axle should be aligned *first?*

_____

20. Always adjust the toe _____.

20. _____

21. In most cases, the ideal alignment setting is in the _____ of a(n) _____ of specifications.

21. _____

_____

22. If camber is adjusted by moving a part in a slotted hole, what is the best procedure for ensuring the adjustment does not move when the attaching bolts are tightened?

_____

_____

_____

23. What should the technician do after making an adjustment and tightening the adjustment fasteners?

_____

24. If rear toe is not evenly divided between each side, a vehicle will have a problem called _____ _____.

24. _____

25. To adjust a vehicle with four-wheel steering, a special tool may be needed to _____ the rear steering gear.

25. _____

26. On some front suspensions, the only alignment angle that can be adjusted is _____.

26. _____

27. Shims are installed between the rear axle and the rear _____ _____. If a(n) _____ _____ shim is used, it can be slipped into place after the bolts are loosened.

27. _____

_____

28. Front caster should be slightly more _____ on the left wheel than the right wheel. The difference, or split, should be no more than _____ degree(s).

28. _____

_____

Name _____

29. In the figure below, the eccentric cam and bolt are used to adjust the front _____.

29. _____

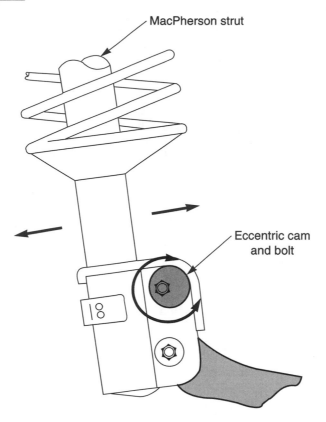

MacPherson strut

Eccentric cam
and bolt

30. In the figure below, moving the strut rod in or out will change _____.

30. _____

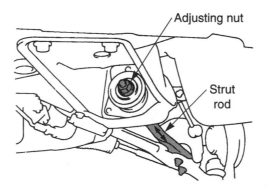

Adjusting nut

Strut
rod

31. To make some adjustments to a MacPherson strut suspension, the adjustment slots must be _____.

31. _____

32. If a vehicle has a conventional suspension, most alignment adjustments are made at the upper or lower _____ _____.

32. _____

33. An experienced technician can adjust _____ and _____ by making one adjustment to conventional suspensions.

33. _____

_____

Name _____

34. To make an adjustment at the control arm shown below, what must be done to the hold-down bolts?
   (A) One bolt must be completely loosened.
   (B) Both bolts must be slightly loosened.
   (C) Both bolts must be removed.
   (D) One bolt must be completely loosened and one bolt must be removed.

34. _____

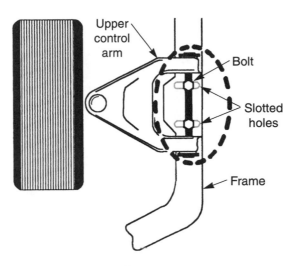

35. If a vehicle has eccentric cams, they are usually located on the _____ control arm.

35. _____

36. On some trucks with solid or twin I-beam axles, the upper ball joint bushings must be replaced with eccentric bushings to adjust what two alignment angles?
   (A) Camber and SAI.
   (B) Caster and SAI.
   (C) Camber and caster.
   (D) Toe and setback.

36. _____

37. If toe is slightly out of adjustment, it can cause excessive _____ wear. If toe is very badly out of adjustment, it can cause _____.

37. _____

   _____

38. Is the toe adjustment device shown in the figure below more commonly used on conventional or rack-and-pinion steering systems?

   _____

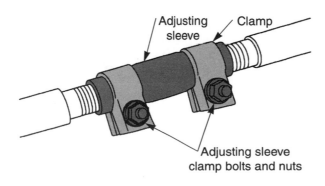

Name _____

39. After making the final alignment checks and adjustments, always _____ _____ the vehicle. Make sure the
_____ _____ is straight and the vehicle does not
_____.

39. _____

_____

_____

40. To straighten a bent vehicle frame, which of the
following should the technician do *first?*
(A) Attach the pulling devices.
(B) Pull the frame into position.
(C) Take frame measurements.
(D) Compare frame measurements with
specifications.

40. _____

Name_____

Date _____ Instructor_____

Score_____ Textbook pages 391–402

Chapter 18

Suspension and Steering Troubleshooting

After studying this chapter, you will be able to:
- ❑ Use the seven-step procedure to troubleshoot suspension and steering problems.
- ❑ Question vehicle drivers concerning suspension and steering problems.
- ❑ Safely road test vehicles to verify suspension and steering system problems.
- ❑ Isolate suspension and steering problems from other vehicle problems.
- ❑ Use correct diagnosis charts and test procedures.
- ❑ Inspect suspension and steering components for complaints related to wear and damage.
- ❑ Determine what repairs must be made to correct suspension and steering problems.
- ❑ Explain the basic principles of noise, vibration, and harshness (NVH) diagnosis.

1. Describe *strategy-based diagnostics.*

_____

_____

_____

Name _____

2. List the seven steps in the diagnosis process in the figure below. Be sure to list the steps in the proper order.

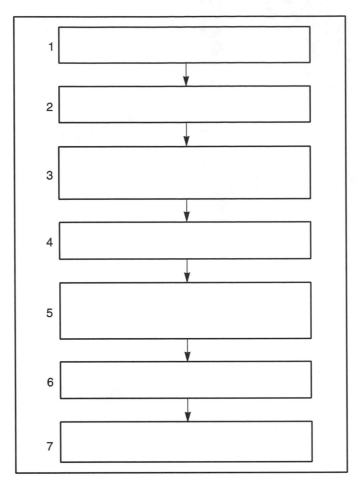

3. When diagnosing a problem, what should the technician question the driver about?

_____

_____

4. To get a better idea of the actual problem, it may help   4. _____
   to write the driver's comments on a(n) _____ _____.

5. Before attempting to road test any vehicle, you should know the answer to the following five questions:

_____

_____

_____

_____

_____

6. All the following are examples of obvious problems   6. _____
   except:
   (A) low tire pressure.
   (B) incorrect tire balance.
   (C) low power steering fluid level.
   (D) weak shock absorbers.

7. During a visual inspection of the steering system, you   7. _____
   should check for leaks at the _____ _____ hoses.

Name _____

8. A power steering pressure test would be *most* likely to be performed in what step of the seven-step troubleshooting process?
   (A) Step 3.
   (B) Step 4.
   (C) Step 5.
   (D) Step 6.

8. _____

9. A warped brake rotor can cause vibration, even when the brakes are released. True or False?

9. _____

10. The real cause of a steering and suspension problem is called the _____ cause.

10. _____

11. A worn ball joint is discovered while troubleshooting a vibration problem. What should the technician do *next*?
    (A) Inform the customer of the problem.
    (B) Check all other suspension and steering parts.
    (C) Find out how much a replacement ball joint costs.
    (D) Replace the ball joint; then check the other parts.

11. _____

12. All the following could be performed in Step 6 of the seven-step procedure *except:*
    (A) tightening a loose nut.
    (B) replacing a defective ball joint.
    (C) adding air to an air shock system.
    (D) measuring tire tread depth.

12. _____

13. While troubleshooting a suspension system problem, you determine that a vehicle needs repairs. What must you *never* assume?

_____

_____

14. Noise, vibration, and harshness (NVH) problems are most often caused by defects in the vehicle's engine or _____ _____. Some NVH problems, however, are caused by defects in the _____ or _____.

14. _____

_____

_____

15. Technician A says small amounts of vehicle vibration are inevitable. Technician B says the best way to fix a vibration problem is to insulate the vibration source. Who is right?
    (A) A only.
    (B) B only.
    (C) Both A and B.
    (D) Neither A nor B.

15. _____

16. Vibrations are transmitted through the vehicle's _____. Most vibrations are caused by parts that _____.

16. _____

_____

17. Complete the following sentences to explain how vibrations are reduced.
    a. By carefully _____ and _____ moving parts.
    b. By placing _____ on rotating parts.
    c. By _____ the body and interior from moving parts.

17. a. _____

_____

b. _____

c. _____

Name _____

18. A first order vibration occurs _____ per revolution.

18. _____

19. The source of almost all noises (and noise complaints) is a(n) _____.

19. _____

20. Excessive play or _____ between two connecting parts can cause noise.

20. _____

21. Describe the neutral run up test.

_____

_____

22. If the vibration is felt during a neutral run up test, the problem is in the _____ or _____.

22. _____

_____

23. Describe the neutral coast down test.

_____

_____

_____

_____

24. All the following statements about noise, vibration, and harshness (NVH) causes are true *except:*
    (A) vibration sources are always moving parts.
    (B) contact between a moving and a non-moving part may cause noise.
    (C) misalignment is often the source of harshness complaints.
    (D) an out-of-balance part can cause an NVH complaint.

24. _____

25. Where should a vibration sensor be attached?

_____

_____

26. Whines or rumbles are usually caused by defects in the _____ or _____.

26. _____

_____

27. Parts that are _____ or _____ usually cause clunking or bumping noises.

27. _____

_____

28. Harshness complaints are usually caused by defects in the _____ system.

28. _____

Chapter 19
ASE Certification

After studying this chapter, you will be able to:
- ❑ Explain why ASE certification is beneficial to both the technician and vehicle owners.
- ❑ Explain the process of registering for ASE tests.
- ❑ Explain how to take the ASE tests.
- ❑ Describe typical ASE test questions.
- ❑ Identify the format of the ASE test results.
- ❑ Explain how the ASE test results are used.

1. The fragmented nature of the automotive industry made automotive repair _____ difficult to set.

1. _____

2. What two things must a technician do before he or she is certified?

_____

_____

3. ASE tests are given _____ each year.

3. _____

4. Who actually administers the ASE tests?
   (A) ASE.
   (B) ACT.
   (C) Local college and university personnel.
   (D) None of the above.

4. _____

5. To register for an ASE test, the technician must have _____.
   (A) several years of work experience
   (B) permission from his or her employer
   (C) proof of citizenship
   (D) a current application form

5. _____

6. The _____ bulletin explains how to fill out the ASE test registration form.

6. _____

Name _____

7. To prepare for the ASE tests, the technician should study all the following *except:*
   (A) basic automotive principles.
   (B) customer relations principles.
   (C) the latest information on automotive diagnosis.
   (D) the latest information on automotive repair techniques.

7. _____

8. You must have your _____ _____ to enter the test center. You must also have a driver's license or another type of _____ identification.

8. _____
   _____

9. Technician A says the test taker should always read the entire question before selecting an answer. Technician B says the test taker should never recheck his or her original answers. Who is right?
   (A) A only.
   (B) B only.
   (C) Both A and B.
   (D) Neither A nor B.

9. _____

10. The question that you are reading now is a(n)_____.
    (A) one-part question
    (B) two-part question
    (C) negative question
    (D) incomplete question

10. _____

11. Two imaginary technicians (Technicians A and B) are always used in a _____-part question.

11. _____

12. A negative question contains the word _____.

12. _____

13. What does the technician receive *before* receiving a test score report?

_____

14. The use of ASE test results is being discussed. Technician A says ASE provides the technician's employer with results if the employer paid for the test. Technician B says ASE will only tell an employer whether or not the technician is certified. Who is right?
    (A) A only.
    (B) B only.
    (C) Both A and B.
    (D) Neither A nor B.

14. _____

15. How many times can a technician take a certification test?

15. _____

Chapter 20
Career Preparation

After studying this chapter, you will be able to:
- ❑ Identify three classifications of automotive technicians.
- ❑ Identify the major sources of employment in the automotive industry.
- ❑ Identify advancement possibilities for automotive technicians.
- ❑ Explain how to fill out a job application.
- ❑ Explain how to conduct oneself during a job interview.

❑ Match the job duties with the type of technician who will *most likely* perform them.

1. Performing alignments.

2. Installing shock absorbers.

3. Changing oil.

4. Installing tires.

5. Diagnosing vehicle problems.

6. Installing alternators.

(A) Helper.

(B) Apprentice technician.

(C) Certified technician.

1. _____

2. _____

3. _____

4. _____

5. _____

6. _____

7. New vehicle dealerships will supply their technician with all the following *except:*
   (A) lifts and floor jacks.
   (B) hand tools.
   (C) special testers.
   (D) cleaning equipment.

7. _____

8. Which of the following is an example of a specialty repair shop?
   (A) Department store automotive center.
   (B) Government garage.
   (C) Import vehicle dealership.
   (D) Alignment shop.

8. _____

Name _____

9. What kinds of repairs are performed at specialty shops?

_____

_____

10. Specialty shops often offer a base salary, as well as a(n) _____ for work performed.

10. _____

11. City garages, state highway department garages, and U.S. Postal Service garages are all examples of _____-operated repair shops.

11. _____

12. All the following statements about automotive management positions are true *except:*
    (A) the manager often has to compromise.
    (B) record keeping will occupy much of the workday.
    (C) the manager spends much of the day performing minor repairs.
    (D) the manager may order shop supplies.

12. _____

13. One of the responsibilities of the _____ _____ is to order out-of-stock automotive parts.

13. _____

14. Technician A says jobs in the automotive service business are hard to find. Technician B says a good place to start your job search is the classified section of your local newspaper. Who is right?
    (A) A only.
    (B) B only.
    (C) Both A and B.
    (D) Neither A nor B.

14. _____

15. All the following help to make a good impression during the job interview *except:*
    (A) dressing neatly.
    (B) arriving a little late.
    (C) not smoking.
    (D) trying to remember the interviewer's name.

15. _____

Instructions for Performing the Workbook Jobs

The jobs in this workbook are designed to supplement the material in the textbook by outlining various hands-on activities. Before starting any job, read through the entire assignment and discuss the procedure with your instructor. It is also important to read the related chapters in the textbook and review all pertinent safety information.

The jobs in this workbook are numbered primarily for ease of reference. The numbers do not necessarily dictate the order in which the jobs must be performed. Some jobs can be done as part of other, more complex jobs. The order in which the jobs are performed is entirely up to the instructor.

Some jobs may take more than one class period to complete. When this occurs, be sure to inform your instructor so your project can be stored properly until you are able to resume work.

As you complete each step in a job, place a check mark in the corresponding box. This will help you keep track of your progress. If any of the steps in a given job do not apply to the particular vehicle or assembly you are working on, mark N/A, for not applicable, by the box. When you finish an entire job, ask you instructor to inspect your work and initial your completed job sheet.

Tools and Materials List

The following is a list of the tools and materials that are used or may be used in the following jobs. In addition to the tools listed here, other special service tools may be specified in the manufacturer's service information. Also, replacement parts will be required on an as-needed basis.

Hand Tools

(Contained in individual sets or the tool crib in sufficient quantities to permit efficient instruction)
Adjustable wrench—6″ and 12″
Air blow gun (meeting OSHA requirements)
Allen (wrench or socket) set—standard (0.050″–3/8″)
Allen (wrench or socket) set—metric (2 mm–7 mm, 10 mm, 12 mm)
Battery post cleaner
Battery terminal pliers
Battery terminal puller
Brake spoon
Chisels:
    cape 5/16″
    cold 3/8″, 3/4″
Chisel holder
Claw type pickup tool
Combination wrenches:
    standard (1/4″ – 1 1/4″)
    metric (7 mm–24 mm)
Crowfoot wrench set—metric
Crowfoot wrench set—standard
Ear protection

Feeler gauge (blade type):
    0.002"–0.040"
    0.006 mm–0.070 mm
Files:
  coarse 6" and 12"
  fine 6" and 12"
  half round 12"
  round 6" and 12"
Flare nut (tubing) wrenches:
  3/8"–3/4"
  10 mm–17 mm
Flashlight
Fuse puller
Hack saw
Hammers:
  16 oz. ball peen
  brass
  dead blow plastic mallet
  plastic tip
  rubber mallet
Inspection mirror
Jumper wire set (with various adapters)
Magnetic pickup tool
Pliers:
  combination 6"
  hose clamp
  locking jaw
  needle nose 6"
  side cutting
  slip joint (water pump)
Pry bars:
  rolling head
  straight
Punches:
  center
  brass drift
  pin 1/8", 3/16", 1/4", 5/16"
  taper 3/8", 1/2", 5/8"
Safety glasses (meeting OSHA requirements)
Scraper:
  carbon 1"
  gasket 1"
Screwdriver—blade type:
  stubby
  6", 9", 12"
  offset
Screwdriver—Phillips:
  stubby #1, #2
  6" #1, #2
  12" #3
  offset #2
Screwdriver—impact driver set
Screw starter:
  Phillips
  standard

Socket set—1/4" drive:
  1/4"–1/2" standard depth
  1/4"–1/2" deep
  6 mm–12 mm standard depth
  6 mm–12 mm deep
  flex/universal type
  3", 6" extensions
  ratchet
Socket set—3/8" drive:
  5/16"–3/4" standard depth (6 point)
  3/8"–3/4" deep (6 point)
  10 mm–19 mm standard depth
  10 mm–19 mm deep
  3", 5", 10" extensions
  flexhead ratchet
  ratchet
  speed handle
  universal joint
  flexible socket set 3/8"–3/4"
  flexible socket set 10 mm–19 mm
Socket set—1/2" drive:
  7/16"–1 1/8" standard depth
  7/16"–1 1/8" deep
  10 mm–24 mm standard depth
  10 mm–24 mm deep
  3", 6", 12" extensions
  flex handle (breaker bar)
  ratchet
Spark plug feeler gauge (gap tool)
Tape measure—standard and metric
Test light (12V)
Tire pressure gauge
Torque wrench:
  3/8" drive (10–250 lb in.)
  3/8" drive (5–75 lb ft.)
  1/2" drive (50–250 lb ft.)
Torx® set (screwdrivers and/or sockets):
  T-8 to T-60
Wire brush

General Lab/Shop Equipment

Air chisel set (various bits)
Air compressor and hoses
Air pressure regulator
Air ratchet (3/8" drive)
Automotive stethoscope (electronic recommended)
Axle stands (safety stands)
Battery charger
Battery/starter/charging system tester
Bearing packer (hand operated)
Belt tension gauge
Bench or pedestal grinder
Brake cleaning equipment (closed system, either
    vacuum or liquid)

Computer scan tool (handheld) or personal computer (PC) with interface capability for on-board diagnostics (OBD II compliant recommended)
Constant velocity joint (CV) service tools:
   boot installation tool
   boot clamp pliers or crimping ring
Creeper
Cylinder leakage tester
Dial indicator with flex arm and clamp base
Digital multi-meter with various lead sets
Drain pans
Drill—3/8" variable speed, reversible
Drill—1/2" variable speed, reversible
Electric heat gun
Disposal contract service
Extension cords
Face shields
Fender covers
Floor jack (1 1/2 ton minimum)
Hand held vacuum pump
Hoist(s)
Hydraulic press with adapters
Impact socket sets—3/8" drive (standard and metric)
Impact sockets—1/2" drive (7/16"–1 1/8")
Impact sockets—1/2" drive (12 mm–24 mm)
Impact sockets—1/2" drive deep (30 mm, 32 mm, 36 mm)
Impact wrench—1/2" drive
Impact wrench—3/8" drive
Jumper cables
Master puller set
Micrometer (depth)
Micrometers—0–1", 1–2", 2–3", 3–4", 4–5" (outside type)
Oil can—pump type
Oxyacetylene torch
Parts cleaning tank and gloves (non-solvent based cleanser suggested)
Screw extractor set
Seat covers
Snap ring pliers set—external
Snap ring pliers set—internal
Tap and die set—standard
Tap and die set—metric
Thread repair insert kit
Tire inflator chuck
Trouble/work lights (fluorescent preferred)
Tubing bender
Tubing cutter/flaring set (double-lap and ISO)
Twist drill set—1/64"–1/2"
Valve core removing tool
Vernier calipers
   0–6"
   0–125 mm
Waste oil receptacle with extension neck and funnel

Wheel chocks
Workbenches with vises

Specialty Tools and Equipment

Ball (small hole) gauges
Ball joint press and other special tools
Battery hydrometer
Bearing seal and race drive set
Brake pedal depressor
Brake shoe adjusting gauge
Brake spring pliers
Brake spring remover/installer
Connector pick tool set
Hand grease gun
Inner tie rod end tool
Inside micrometer set:
   0–125 mm
   0–6"
Outside micrometer set:
   0–125 mm
   0–6"
Pitman arm puller
Portable crane—1/2 ton
Power steering pump pulley special tool set (appropriate for units being taught)
Refrigerant charging station (R-12 and HFC-134a) or equivalent
Refrigerant recovery/recycling machine (R-12 and HFC-134a)
Shock absorber tools
Spring/strut compressor tool
Static strap
Steering column special tool set (appropriate for teaching units being utilized)
Straightedge
Telescopic gauge set
Tie rod puller
Tire mounting machine (rim clamp suggested)
Universal joint tools
Vacuum/pressure gauge
Wheel alignment equipment—4 wheel (including alignment tools)
Wheel balancer—electronic type
Wheel weight pliers
Wire and terminal repair kit

Additional Materials

Applicable service manuals or information system
Approved lubricants
Approved parts cleaners
Chemical sealers and adhesives
Miscellaneous replacement gaskets
Miscellaneous replacement seals

Name _____ Date _____

Score _____ Instructor _____

Shop Safety

Objective

After studying related textbook material and satisfactorily performing this task, you will be able to identify and correct safety hazards in the automotive shop.

Warning: *Before performing this job, review all pertinent safety information in the text and discuss safety procedures with your instructor.*

Procedure

1. Walk around your automotive shop and look for fire hazards, including:
   - Missing or inoperative fire extinguishers. (Check extinguisher tags to determine whether the extinguisher should be recharged.)
   - Leaking fuel or lubricant containers.
   - Oily rags stored in unapproved containers.
   - Excessive litter.
   - Unshielded heat sources (heaters, torches, etc.).
   - No fire or emergency evacuation plan.

   Describe any unsafe conditions found.

   Completed ❏

   _____

   _____

   _____

   _____

2. Inspect the tools found in your shop for defects, including the following:
   - Loose or broken handles on hammers and other striking tools.
   - Worn or damaged teeth on wrenches and sockets.
   - Cracked sockets.
   - Unsafe electrical tools.
   - Mushroomed chisel heads.
   - Leaking hydraulic jacks.

   Completed ❏

Name _____

- Damaged jack stands.
- Defective vehicle lifts.

In the blanks below, describe any problems found.

_____
_____
_____
_____

3. Walk around your shop and look for electrical
   hazards, such as: Completed ❑
   - Missing ground plugs on electrical tools.
   - Overloaded electrical sockets.
   - Frayed or damaged cords.
   - Exposed light sockets or broken bulbs.
   - Exposed electrical wiring.
   - Wet floors.

In the blanks below, describe any problems found.

_____
_____
_____
_____

4. List several ways air can be polluted by an automotive   Completed ❑
   shop and note whether these could occur in your
   shop.

_____
_____
_____
_____

5. List the types of solid waste produced by your shop.   Completed ❑

_____
_____
_____
_____

6. From the solid waste list compiled in Step 5, identify   Completed ❑
   the types of waste that can be recycled.

_____
_____
_____
_____
_____

Name _____

7. From the solid waste list compiled in Step 6, identify   Completed ❑
   the types of waste that can be returned for a core
   deposit.

   _____

   _____

   _____

   _____

8. Describe several ways improper suspension and   Completed ❑
   steering procedures can cause an accident.

   _____

   _____

   _____

   _____

   _____

   _____

   _____

   _____

Job 2

Checking for Worn or Bent Suspension Parts

Objective

After studying related textbook material and satisfactorily performing this job, you will be able to use visual and manual techniques to determine the condition of suspension parts.

> **Note:** *For a complete suspension and steering checking procedure, refer to Job 15.*

Materials and Equipment

- Vehicle in need of suspension system service
- Lift or floor jack and jack stands
- Safety stands as needed
- Dial indicator
- Service manuals or other service literature as needed

> **Warning:** *Before performing this job, review all pertinent safety information in the text and discuss safety procedures with your instructor.*

Procedure

1. Obtain the service manual for the vehicle being serviced.   Completed ❑

2. Raise the front of the vehicle so the front suspension is correctly suspended for checking the ball joints.   Completed ❑

   Where did you place the jack or lifting arm?

   _____

   _____

Name _____

3. Check all *front* suspension parts for damage and complete the following chart. Write "NA" in the first blank when the part is not used on the vehicle you are checking.

Completed ❑

	Passed	Worn/Loose	Bent/Broken	Leaking
Upper ball joints				
Upper control arms				
Control arm bushings				
Strut rod				
Strut rod bushings				
Stabilizer bar				
Stabilizer bar bushings				
Shock absorbers				
Strut cartridges				
Springs/Torsion bars				
Fasteners				
Frame/Subframe				

What do you think caused the defect(s) (if defects were detected)?

_____

_____

4. Shake both front wheels and note any looseness. See **Figure 1.**

Completed ❑

Was any looseness detected? _____

What should you do next? _____

_____

Figure 1. *When checking for loose suspension parts, grasp the wheel as shown and try to shake it. Slight movement is normal. If the wheel moves excessively, check for worn ball joints or bushings.*

Name _____

5. Have a helper shake each front wheel while you
   observe the front suspension.   Completed ❑

   Were there any loose parts? _____ If so, list them in the following blanks.

   Front left side: _____

   _____

   Front right side: _____

   _____

   What do these conditions indicate? _____

   _____

   What should you do next? _____

   _____

6. Obtain a dial indicator and use it to check ball joint
   play, **Figure 2.**   Completed ❑

   > Note: *Checking ball joint play may not be necessary on the vehicle you are
   > servicing. Check with your instructor.*

   Specified maximum ball joint play: _____

   Actual ball joint play: _____

   Is ball joint play within specifications? _____

   _____

   What should you do next? _____

   _____

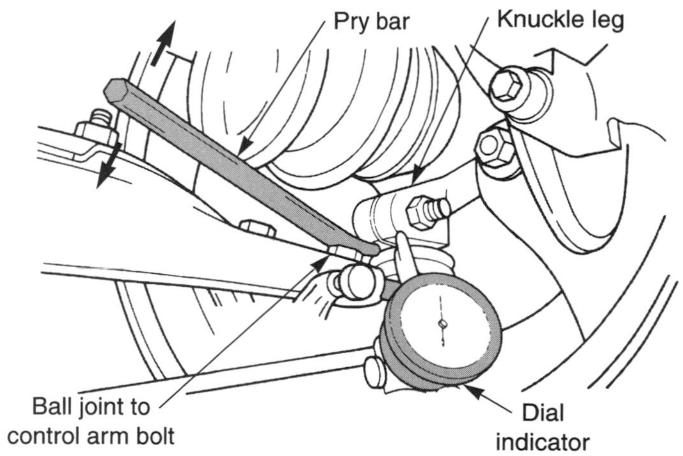

Figure 2. *When using a dial indicator to check ball joint play, use a pry bar to pry between the steering knuckle and the control arm. (Sealed Power)*

7. Raise the rear of the vehicle so the rear suspension
   parts can be checked.   Completed ❑

   Where did you place the jack or lifting arm? _____

   _____

Name _____

8. Check all *rear* suspension parts for damage and complete the following chart. Write "NA" in the first blank when the part is not used on the vehicle you are checking.   Completed ❑

	Passed	Worn/Loose	Bent/Broken	Leaking
Lower ball joints				
Lower control arms				
Strut rod				
Strut rod bushings				
Stabilizer bar				
Stabilizer bar bushings				
Shock absorbers				
Strut cartridges				
Springs/Torsion bars				
Fasteners				
Axle				

What do you think caused the defect(s) (if defects were detected)? _____

_____

_____

9. If the vehicle is equipped with rear lower ball joints, check them for looseness as specified by the service manual.   Completed ❑

Specified maximum ball joint play: _____

Actual ball joint play: _____

Is ball joint play within specifications? _____

What should you do next? _____

10. With your instructors approval, make needed repairs based on your front and rear suspension inspections.   Completed ❑

What repairs were made? _____

_____

_____

11. Recheck the condition of the suspension system. If the problem has been corrected, go to Step 12. If the problem still exists, what should you do next?   Completed ❑

_____

_____

12. Return all tools and equipment to storage and clean the work area.   Completed ❑

Name _____

13. Did you encounter any problems during the inspec-   Completed ❑
    tion or repair procedure? _____

    If so, describe the problems encountered. _____

    _____

    What did you do to correct them? _____

    _____

Optional Procedure

> Note: *The following procedure will be performed at the option of your instructor.*

Objective

After studying related textbook material and satisfactorily performing this task, you will be able to check vehicle ride height.

Materials and Equipment

- Vehicle
- Alignment rack or level floor
- Tape measure
- Service manuals or other literature

> **Warning:** *Before performing this job, review all pertinent safety information in the text and review safety information with your instructor.*

Name _____

1. Consult the correct service manual for the ride height specifications and measuring points. See **Figure 3.**   Completed ❑

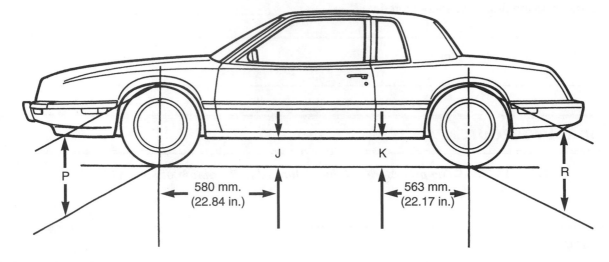

Rocker panel		Wheel opening	
J	K	P	R
219	222	696	705
8.62	8.74	27.40	27.76

Figure 3. *Ride height specifications of one particular vehicle. Ride height varies from one vehicle to another. Always consult the appropriate manual for the vehicle being serviced. (General Motors)*

2. Place the vehicle on the alignment rack or on a flat portion of the shop floor.   Completed ❑

3. Make sure all tires are the same size and type.   Completed ❑

4. Check and adjust air pressure.   Completed ❑

5. Check the trunk and backseat for extra weight and remove weight, if necessary.   Completed ❑

6. Locate the ride height measuring points on the vehicle's body or frame. Where are the ride height measuring points?   Completed ❑

   Front: _____

   Rear: _____

7. Check ride height by measuring between the specified measuring point and the rack or floor. Record your measurements in the following spaces: Completed ❑

   Left Front: _____

   Right Front: _____

   Left Rear: _____

   Right Rear: _____

Name _____

8. Compare the ride height measurements with the specifications.   Completed ❑

   Were any ride height measurements out of specification? _____

   If so, which ones were incorrect? _____

   _____

9. Compare the ride height measurements from the left and right sides of the vehicle. Is there more than 1/4″ (0.6 mm) variation? _____   Completed ❑

10. If ride height is incorrect, what can be done to correct the problem? _____   Completed ❑

    _____

11. Make necessary adjustments or repairs to correct ride height.   Completed ❑

12. After making needed adjustments or repairs, recheck the ride height and record your measurements   Completed ❑

    Left Front: _____

    Right Front: _____

    Left Rear: _____

    Right Rear: _____

    Is the ride height correct? _____

    If ride height is correct, go to Step 13. If ride height is incorrect, what should you do next?

    _____

    _____

13. Return all tools and equipment to storage and clean the work area.   Completed ❑

14. Did you encounter any problems during the inspection or repair procedure? _____   Completed ❑

    If so, describe the problems encountered. _____

    _____

    What did you do to correct them? _____

    _____

Name _____ Date _____

Score_____ Instructor _____

Job **3**

Replacing Shock Absorbers

Objective

After studying related textbook material and satisfactorily performing this task, you will be able to remove and replace shock absorbers used on vehicles with conventional suspension.

Materials and Equipment

- Vehicle in need of shock absorber replacement
- Lift or floor jack and jack stands
- Replacement shock absorbers
- Air-operated tools as needed
- Hand tools as needed
- Correct service literature

> **Warning:** *Before performing this job, review all pertinent safety information in the text and discuss safety procedures with your instructor.*

Procedure

> **Note:** *This procedure applies to front or rear shocks. Some steps apply to specific front or rear axle procedures.*

1. Safely raise the vehicle.   Completed ❑

   Why are the shock absorbers being replaced? _____

   _____

2. On rear axles, make sure the axle will not drop when   Completed ❑
   the shock absorbers are removed. If necessary,
   support the rear axle with jack stands.

3. Remove the fasteners holding the shock absorber to   Completed ❑
   the vehicle. See **Figure 1.**

   What kind of fasteners hold the shock absorber to the vehicle?

      Upper: _____

      Lower: _____

Name _____

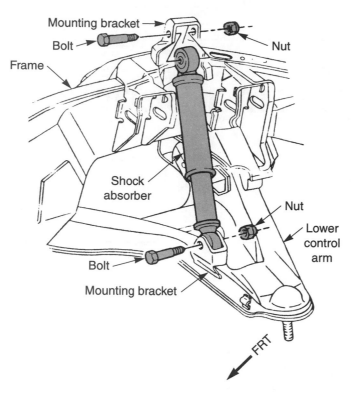

Figure 1. *Shock absorber mountings vary from one type vehicle to another. This particular shock absorber is attached to the frame and control arm with bolts that pass through rubber bushings. (General Motors)*

> **Note: *If the rear shock absorbers are air operated, depressurize the system and remove the air lines at this time.***

4. Remove the shock absorber from the vehicle.   Completed ❑

5. Compare the old and new shock absorbers.   Completed ❑

> **Note: *If the shocks do not match, obtain the correct shocks before proceeding.***

6. Place the new shock absorbers in position.   Completed ❑

> **Note: *It may be necessary to compress the new shock absorber slightly to place it in position.***

7. Install the shock absorber fasteners.   Completed ❑

8. Repeat Steps 2–7 for other shock absorbers to be changed.   Completed ❑

    How many shock absorbers were changed? _____

9. Lower the vehicle and check shock absorber operation.   Completed ❑

10. Return all tools and equipment to storage and clean the work area.   Completed ❑

11. Did you encounter any problems during the inspection or repair procedure? _____ Completed ❑

    If so, describe the problems encountered. _____

    _____

    What did you do to correct them? _____

    _____

Replacing MacPherson Strut Assemblies

Objective

After studying related textbook material and satisfactorily performing this task, you will be able to remove and replace MacPherson strut assemblies.

Materials and Equipment

- Vehicle in need of MacPherson strut replacement
- Lift or floor jack and jack stands
- MacPherson strut compressor
- Replacement MacPherson strut cartridges
- Air-operated tools as needed
- Hand tools as needed
- Correct service manual

    Warning: *Before performing this job, review all pertinent safety information in the text and discuss safety procedures with your instructor.*

Procedure

Note: *This procedure is general in nature. Note that some MacPherson struts are attached by different methods, and some vehicles have the spring separate from the strut assembly. On other vehicles, the strut cartridge can be removed from under the hood. Always consult the proper service manual before proceeding with replacement. After strut replacement, the vehicle must be realigned.*

1. Safely raise the vehicle.   Completed ❑

    Why are the struts being changed? _____

    _____

2. Remove the wheel and tire.   Completed ❑

3. Remove the fasteners holding the strut assembly to   Completed ❑
   the vehicle.

    Do the upper or lower strut mountings have a provision for alignment adjustment? _____

Name _____

If so, describe how alignment is adjusted. _____

_____

_____

What should you do to make sure the alignment is as close as possible to the original settings? _____

_____

4. Remove the strut assembly from the vehicle.   Completed ❑

5. Place the strut assembly in the strut compressor. See   Completed ❑
   Figure 1.

   Why should you mark the spring and cartridge before compressing the spring? _____

   _____

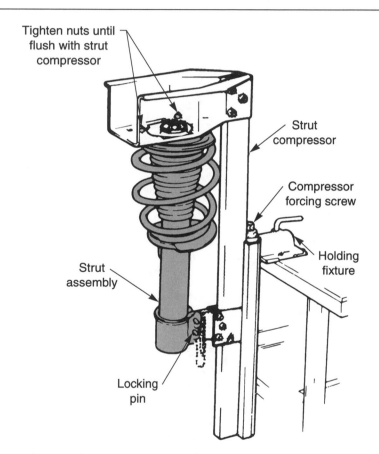

Figure 1. *A strut must be mounted in an appropriate compressor before disassembly. (General Motors)*

6. Compress the strut assembly spring.   Completed ❑

7. Remove the upper shaft nut and remove the cartridge   Completed ❑
   assembly from the spring.

8. Compare the new strut cartridge to the old one.   Completed ❑

   Note: *If the cartridges do not match, obtain the correct cartridges before*
   proceeding.

9. Place the new cartridge in position inside the spring.   Completed ❑

10. Install and tighten the upper shaft nut.   Completed ❑

Name _____

11. Decompress the spring, making sure all parts are properly aligned.   Completed ❏

12. Remove the strut assembly from the compressor and place it in position on the vehicle.   Completed ❏

13. Install and tighten the strut fasteners.   Completed ❏

14. Repeat Steps 2–12 to replace the other strut cartridge.   Completed ❏

15. Lower the vehicle and check strut operation.   Completed ❏

16. Return all tools and equipment to storage and clean the work area.   Completed ❏

17. Did you encounter any problems during this procedure? _____   Completed ❏

    If so, describe the problems and explain what you did to correct them._____

    _____

    _____

    _____

Replacing Ball Joints

Objective

After studying related textbook material and satisfactorily performing this task, you will be able to remove and replace upper or lower ball joints.

Materials and Equipment

- Vehicle in need of ball joint service
- Lift or floor jack and jack stands
- Ball joint removal tools
- Replacement ball joints
- Air-operated tools as needed
- Hand tools as needed
- Correct service literature

  Warning: *Before performing this job, review all pertinent safety information in the text and discuss safety procedures with your instructor.*

Procedure

Note: *After ball joints are replaced, the vehicle must be aligned. Your instructor may direct you to perform Job 15.*

1. Safely raise the vehicle.   Completed ❑

   Which ball joints are being replaced?

   Upper: _____

   Lower: _____

2. Remove the wheel and tire.   Completed ❑

3. Place a stand under the lower control arm.   Completed ❑

4. Remove the cotter pin from the nut of the ball joint to   Completed ❑
   be replaced.

   Is this ball joint a loaded joint or a follower joint? _____

   If it is loaded, is it tension loaded or compression loaded? _____

Name _____

5. Loosen the ball joint but do not remove it.   Completed ❑

6. Break the ball joint-to-steering knuckle taper using a   Completed ❑
   hammer or a special tool as shown in **Figure 1.**

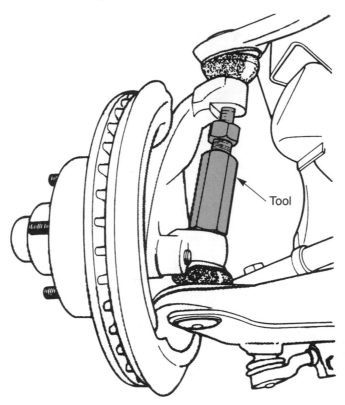
Tool

Figure 1. *Using a special tool to break the ball joint-to-steering knuckle taper. (General Motors)*

7. Remove the nut from the ball joint stud.   Completed ❑

   > **Caution:** *If the spring is installed on the lower control arm, support the arm*
   > *before removing the nut. This should be done even when the upper ball joint*
   > *is being replaced.*

8. Remove the steering knuckle from the ball joint stud.   Completed ❑

9. Remove the ball joint from the control arm.   Completed ❑

   > **Note:** *There are many ball joint attachment methods. Consult the service*
   > *manual if you have any doubts as to the correct method.*

   How are the ball joints attached (bolts, pressed in, other)? _____

   How did you remove them? _____

10. Compare the old and new ball joints.   Completed ❑

    Is the new ball joint the same design as the old ball joint? _____

    > **Caution:** *Do not attempt to install an incorrect ball joint.*

11. Install the new ball joint in the control arm.   Completed ❑

    What is the attachment method? _____

    Does this differ from the original attachment method? _____

    If yes, how? _____

12. Install the ball joint stud in the steering knuckle.   Completed ❑

Name _____

13. Install the nut on the ball joint stud.   Completed ❑

14. Install a new cotter pin. See **Figure 2.**   Completed ❑

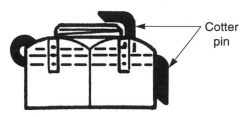

Cotter
pin

Figure 2. *When installing a new cotter pin, be sure to bend the pin as shown to prevent it from falling out. (General Motors)*

15. Install the wheel and tire.   Completed ❑

16. Lubricate the new ball joint if it has a grease fitting.   Completed ❑

    Does the ball joint have a grease fitting? _____

17. Repeat Steps 2–16 to replace other ball joints as   Completed ❑
    needed.

18. Lower the vehicle.   Completed ❑

19. Return all tools and equipment to storage and clean   Completed ❑
    the work area.

20. Did you encounter any problems during this   Completed ❑
    procedure? _____

    If so, describe the problems and explain what you did to correct them. _____

    _____

    _____

    _____

Replacing Control Arms and Bushings

Objective

After studying related textbook material and satisfactorily performing this task, you will be able to remove and replace an upper or lower control arm, and remove and replace control arm bushings.

Materials and Equipment

- Vehicle in need of control arm or bushing service
- Lift or floor jack and jack stands
- Bushing drivers
- Replacement bushings
- Air-operated tools as needed
- Hand tools as needed
- Correct service literature

> **Warning:** *Before performing this job, review all pertinent safety information in the text and discuss safety procedures with your instructor.*

Procedure

> **Note:** *After the control arm or bushings are replaced, the vehicle must be aligned. Check with your instructor to determine whether you should perform Job 18 after completing this job.*

1. Raise the vehicle so the control arm is free. Completed ❑

2. Remove the wheel and tire. Completed ❑

   > **Warning:** *If the control arm is under spring tension, be sure to place a jack stand under the control arm.*

3. Remove the ball joint stud from the steering knuckle as covered in Job 5. Completed ❑

   > **Warning:** *If you are changing a control arm that is under spring pressure, the tension must be removed before loosening any fasteners. Follow the manufacturer's recommendations when using the spring compressor.*

4. Remove the strut rod, stabilizer bar, alignment shims, and shock absorber mounting as necessary. Completed ❑

Name _____

Which of the parts listed in Step 4 required removal? _____

_____

5. Remove the control arm or cross bar attaching bolts.   Completed ❑

   Are there any eccentric cams on the control arm bolts? _____

   Is the cross bar attached by bolts passing through slotted holes? _____

   Did you mark the relative position of these parts for reassembly? _____

6. Remove the control arm from the vehicle.   Completed ❑

7. Place the control arm in a vise.   Completed ❑

8. Remove the bushings using a special tool or an air   Completed ❑
   chisel. See **Figure 1.**

   Briefly describe how you removed the bushings. _____

   _____

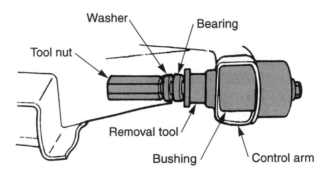

Figure 1. *A special press can be used to remove bushings from a control arm. After the press is installed, turning the nut will force the bushing from the control arm. (General Motors)*

9. Compare the old and new bushings.   Completed ❑

10. Install the new bushings using the proper driver.   Completed ❑

    Briefly describe how you installed the bushings. _____

    _____

11. Replace the control arm on the vehicle.   Completed ❑

12. Install the fasteners at the control arm bushings or   Completed ❑
    cross bar.

13. Install all related parts.   Completed ❑

14. Install the ball joint on the steering knuckle.   Completed ❑

15. Install the ball joint nut and a new cotter pin.   Completed ❑

16. Install the wheel and tire.   Completed ❑

17. Repeat steps 2 through 16 to replace other control   Completed ❑
    arms or control arm bushings as needed.

18. Lower the vehicle.   Completed ❑

19. Return all tools and equipment to storage and clean   Completed ❑
    the work area.

Name _____

20. Did you encounter any problems during this   Completed ❑
    procedure? _____

    If so, describe the problems and explain what you did to correct them. _____

    _____

    _____

    _____

Name _____ Date _____

Score _____ Instructor _____

Job 7

Replacing Strut Rods, Stabilizer Bars, and Bushings

Objective

After studying related textbook material and satisfactorily performing this task, you will be able to remove and replace strut rods, stabilizer bars, and related bushings.

Materials and Equipment

- Vehicle in need of strut rod, stabilizer bar, or bushing service
- Lift or floor jack and jack stands
- Replacement bushings or other parts
- Air-operated tools as needed
- Hand tools as needed
- Correct service literature

> **Warning:** *Before performing this job, review all pertinent safety information in the text and discuss safety procedures with your instructor.*

Procedure

> **Note:** *After the strut rod or bushings are replaced, the vehicle must be aligned. Check with your instructor to determine whether you should perform Job 18 after completing this job. Alignment is usually not necessary after stabilizer bar service.*

Strut Rod Service

1. Safely raise the vehicle.   Completed ❑

2. Remove the strut rod mounting at the control arm.   Completed ❑
   See **Figure 1.**

   How was the arm mounted to the control arm? _____

   _____

   Is this where the bushing is located? _____

   Are there any provisions for adjustment? _____

Name _____

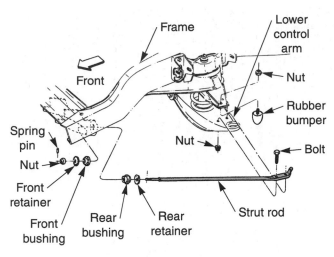

Figure 1. *This particular strut rod is bolted to the control arm. (Dodge)*

3. Remove the strut rod mounting at the frame.   Completed ❑

   Is the strut rod threaded for adjustment at the frame? _____

   Did you mark the relative position of these parts for reassembly? _____

4. Remove the strut rod from the vehicle.   Completed ❑

5. Remove the bushings from the frame or control arm   Completed ❑
   as necessary.

6. Compare the old and new bushings.   Completed ❑

7. Install the new bushings in the frame or control arm.   Completed ❑

   Briefly describe how you installed the bushings. _____

   _____

   _____

8. Reinstall the strut rod on the vehicle.   Completed ❑

9. Reinstall and tighten all fasteners.   Completed ❑

10. Repeat steps 2 through 9 to replace other strut rods as   Completed ❑
    needed.

11. Lower the vehicle.   Completed ❑

12. Return all tools and equipment to storage and clean   Completed ❑
    the work area.

13. Did you encounter any problems during this   Completed ❑
    procedure? _____

    If so, describe the problems and explain what you did to correct them.

    _____

    _____

    _____

Name _____

Stabilizer Bar Service

1. Raise the vehicle on a lift or place it on jack stands.   Completed ❑

2. Remove the stabilizer bar mounting at each control   Completed ❑
   arm. See **Figure 2.**

   How was the bar mounted to the control arm?_____

   _____

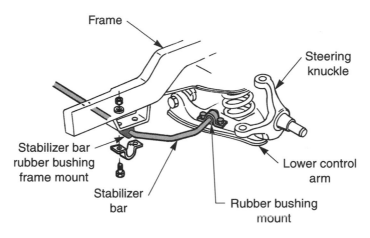

Figure 2. *This stabilizer bar is mounted to the control arm and held in place with a rubber bushing. (Moog)*

3. Remove the stabilizer bar mountings at the frame.   Completed ❑

4. Remove the stabilizer bar from the vehicle.   Completed ❑

5. Remove the bushings from the stabilizer bar mountings.   Completed ❑

6. Compare the old and new bushings.   Completed ❑

7. Install the new bushings on the stabilizer bar mountings.   Completed ❑

   Briefly describe how you installed the bushings. _____

   _____

8. Reinstall the stabilizer bar on the vehicle.   Completed ❑

9. Reinstall and tighten all fasteners.   Completed ❑

10. Lower the vehicle.   Completed ❑

11. Return all tools and equipment to storage and clean   Completed ❑
    the work area.

12. Did you encounter any problems during this   Completed ❑
    procedure? _____

    If so, describe the problems and explain what you did to correct them. _____

    _____

    _____

    _____

Name _____ Date _____

Score _____ Instructor _____

Checking for Worn or Bent Steering Parts

Objective

After studying related textbook material and satisfactorily performing this task, you will be able to use visual and manual techniques to determine the condition of steering parts.

Note: *For a complete suspension and steering checking procedure, refer to Job 17, Diagnosing Suspension and Steering Problems.*

Materials and Equipment

- Vehicle in need of steering system service
- Rack or lifting equipment
- Safety stands as needed
- Dial indicator
- Service manuals or other service literature as needed

    Warning: *Before performing this job, review all pertinent safety information in the text and discuss safety procedures with your instructor.*

Procedure

1. Obtain the proper service manual for the system.   Completed ❑

2. Raise the vehicle so the steering system is free to turn.   Completed ❑

    Where did you place the jack or lifting arm? _____

    _____

3. Check the steering linkage and steering gear, and steering shaft for damage. Complete the chart on page 132. Write "NA" in the first column when the part is not used on the vehicle you are checking.   Completed ❑

Name _____

	Passed	Worn/Loose	Bent/Broken	Leaking
Steering arms				
Outer tie rod ends				
Inner tie rod ends				
Pitman arm				
Idler arm				
Relay rod/drag link				
Steering gear				
Steering coupler				
Steering shaft				
Power steering pump				
Power steering belt				
Power steering hoses				
Fasteners				

What do you think caused the defects (if defects were detected)?

_____

_____

4. Shake both front wheels and note any looseness.   Completed ❑

Was any looseness detected? _____

If so, what should you do next? _____

_____

5. Have a helper shake each front wheel and observe   Completed ❑
the steering linkage.

Describe any loose parts.

Front left side: _____

_____

_____

Front right side: _____

_____

_____

What do these conditions indicate? _____

_____

What should you do next? _____

_____

6. If necessary, check the rear steering linkage for   Completed ❑
damage. Complete the chart on page 133. Write "NA"
in the first column when the part is not used on the
vehicle you are checking.

Name _____

	Passed	Worn/Loose	Bent/Broken	Leaking
Steering arms				
Outer tie rod ends				
Inner tie rod ends				
Steering gear				
Power steering hoses				
Hydraulic valves				
Electrical controls				
Fasteners				

What do you think caused the defects (if defects were detected)?

_____

_____

7. With your instructor's approval, make needed repairs.   Completed ❑

What repairs were made? _____

_____

_____

8. Recheck steering system condition.   Completed ❑

Was the problem corrected? _____

If so, go to Step 9. If the problem still exists, what should you do next?

_____

_____

9. Return all tools and equipment to storage and clean   Completed ❑
   the work area.

10. Did you encounter any problems during this   Completed ❑
    procedure? _____

If so, describe the problems and explain what you did to correct them. _____

_____

_____

_____

Job **9**

Removing and Replacing Tie Rod Ends

Objective

After studying related textbook material and satisfactorily performing this task, you will be able to remove and replace inner and outer tie rod ends.

Materials and Equipment

- Vehicle in need of tie rod replacement
- Lift or floor jack and jack stands
- Replacement tie rods
- Air-operated tools as needed
- Hand tools as needed
- Correct service literature

> **Warning:** *Before performing this job, review all pertinent safety information in the text and discuss safety procedures with your instructor.*

Procedure

> **Note:** *After any tie rod is replaced, the vehicle must be aligned. Check with your instructor to determine whether you should perform Job 18 after completing this job.*

All except Rack-and-Pinion Inner Tie Rod Ends

1. Safely raise the vehicle.   Completed ❏

   Which tie rod(s) will be replaced? _____

   _____

2. Remove the cotter pin from the nut holding the tie rod   Completed ❏
   end to be replaced.

3. Remove the tie rod nut.   Completed ❏

Name _____

4. Break the tie rod stud taper using a special tool or a hammer. See **Figure 1.**

   Completed ❑

   How did you break the taper? _____

   _____

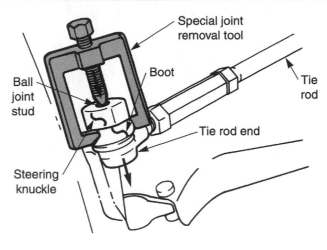

Figure 1. *Using a tie rod removal tool to break the tie rod stud taper. (General Motors)*

5. Loosen the fastener holding the tie rod to the steering linkage.

   Completed ❑

   How is the tie rod fastened to the linkage? _____

   _____

6. Mark the relative position of the tie rod end for reassembly.

   Completed ❑

7. Unscrew the tie rod end from the linkage.

   Completed ❑

8. Compare the old and new tie rod ends.

   Completed ❑

9. Install the new tie rod end.

   Completed ❑

10. Tighten the fasteners and install a new cotter pin.

    Completed ❑

11. Repeat Steps 2–10 for other tie rod ends to be changed.

    Completed ❑

    How many tie rod ends were changed? _____

12. Lower the vehicle and check steering system operation.

    Completed ❑

13. Return all tools and equipment to storage and clean the work area.

    Completed ❑

14. Did you encounter any problems during this procedure? _____

    Completed ❑

    If so, describe the problems. _____

    _____

    What did you do to correct them? _____

    _____

Name _____

Rack-and-Pinion Inner Tie Rod Ends

1. Raise the vehicle on a lift or place it on jack stands.   Completed ❑

2. Loosen the outer tie rod locknut.   Completed ❑

3. Disconnect the outer tie rod.   Completed ❑

4. Remove the bellows boot from the steering gear and   Completed ❑
    inner tie rod.

    How was the boot held to the steering gear? _____

    _____

    How was the boot held to the tie rod? _____

    _____

    How did you remove them? _____

    _____

5. Turn the steering gear until the inner tie rod is fully   Completed ❑
    exposed.

6. Remove the pin, washer, or crimp holding the inner   Completed ❑
    tie rod to the rack assembly. See **Figure 2.**

    How is the inner tie rod fastened to the rack? _____

    How did you remove the fasteners? _____

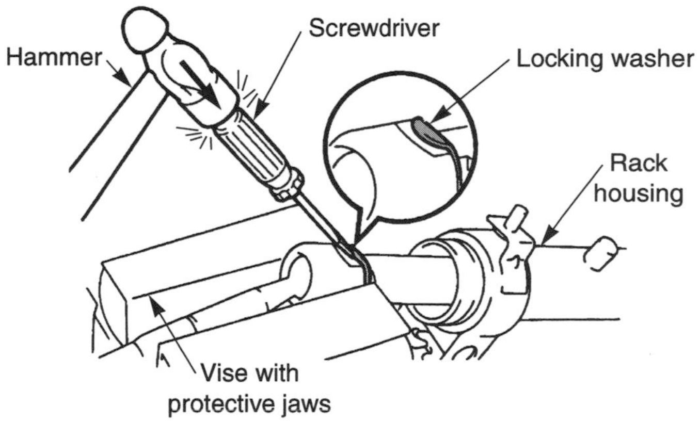

Figure 2. *A small chisel or screwdriver can be used to remove the locking washer that secures the inner tie rod to the rack. Be careful not to damage the rack. (Toyota)*

7. Install wrench or a special tool over the inner tie rod   Completed ❑
    end.

8. Place a large adjustable wrench on the rack to keep it   Completed ❑
    from turning.

9. Unscrew the inner tie rod from the rack.   Completed ❑

10. Compare the old and new tie rod ends.   Completed ❑

11. Use the wrench or special tool to install the new tie   Completed ❑
    rod end.

12. Crimp the new tie rod end to the rack, **Figure 3,** or   Completed ❑
    install the locking pin.

Name _____

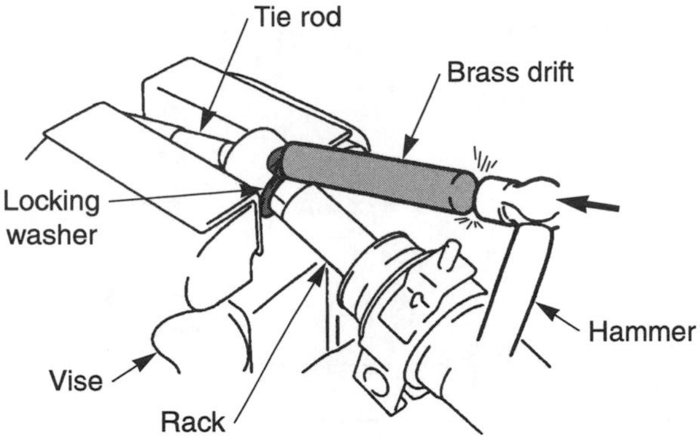

Figure 3. *Using a brass drift to crimp the locking washer. Crimping the washer prevents the tie rod from loosening. (Toyota)*

13. Repeat Steps 2–12 to change the tie rod ends on the opposite side (if necessary).   Completed ❏

    How many tie rod ends were changed? _____

14. Lower the vehicle and check steering system operation.   Completed ❏

15. Return all tools and equipment to storage and clean the work area.   Completed ❏

16. Did you encounter any problems during this procedure? _____   Completed ❏

    If so, describe the problems and explain what you did to correct them. _____

    _____

    _____

    _____

Removing and Replacing Steering Linkage

Objective

After studying related textbook material and satisfactorily performing this task, you will be able to remove and replace pitman arms, idler arms, relay rods/drag links, and related linkage parts.

Materials and Equipment

- Vehicle in need of steering linkage replacement
- Lift or floor jack and jack stands
- Replacement parts
- Air-operated tools as needed
- Hand tools as needed
- Correct service literature

> **Warning: Before performing this job, review all pertinent safety information in the text and discuss safety procedures with your instructor.**

Procedure

> **Note: After any steering linkage part is replaced, the vehicle must be aligned. Check with your instructor to determine whether you should perform Job 18 after completing this job.**

1. Safely raise the vehicle.   Completed ❑

   Which steering part(s) will be replaced? _____

   _____

2. Remove the cotter pin from the nut(s) holding ball   Completed ❑
   socket(s) of the part to be replaced.

3. Remove the nut(s) from the ball socket(s).   Completed ❑

4. Break the stud tapers as necessary using a special tool   Completed ❑
   or a hammer.

   How did you break the tapers? _____

   _____

Name _____

5. Loosen and remove the fasteners holding the part to the frame or steering gear, if applicable.   Completed ❏

   How is the part fastened to the frame or gear? _____

6. Remove the part from the vehicle. See **Figure 1.**   Completed ❏

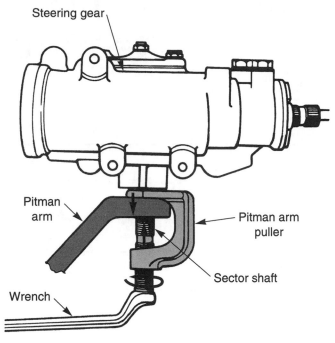

Figure 1. *Special tools must be used to remove some steering system parts. For example, a pitman arm puller must be used to remove the pitman arm from the steering gear sector shaft. (Dodge)*

7. Compare the old and new parts.   Completed ❏

8. Install the new part on the vehicle.   Completed ❏

9. Install and tighten all fasteners and install new cotter pins as necessary.   Completed ❏

10. Repeat Steps 2–9 for other linkage parts to be changed.   Completed ❏

11. Lower the vehicle and check steering system operation.   Completed ❏

12. Return all tools and equipment to storage and clean the work area.   Completed ❏

13. Did you encounter any problems during this procedure? _____   Completed ❏

   If so, describe the problems and explain what you did to correct them. _____

   _____

   _____

   _____

Testing Power Steering System Operation

Objective

After studying related textbook material and satisfactorily performing this job, you will be able to test the operation of power steering systems.

Materials and Equipment

- Vehicle with power steering system
- Power steering pressure gauges
- Hand tools as needed
- Correct service literature

    Warning: *Before performing this job, review all pertinent safety information in the text and discuss safety procedures with your instructor.*

Procedure

1. Open the hood and make a preliminary check of the power steering system. See **Figures 1** and **2.**   Completed ❑

    Complete the following:

    Power steering reservoir level:

    Between full and add marks _____ Below add mark _____

    Power steering fluid condition:

    Good _____ Burned _____ Discolored _____ Contaminated _____

    Pump drive belt condition:

    Tight _____ Loose _____ Glazed _____ Missing _____

    Evidence of leaks:

    No _____ Yes _____ Possible source _____

Name _____

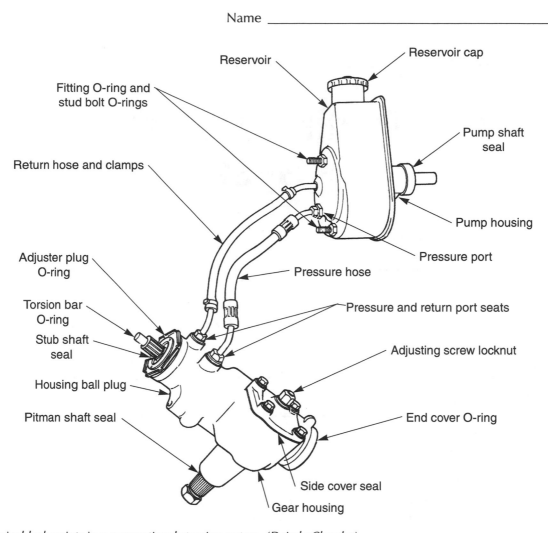

Figure 1. *Typical leak points in a conventional steering system. (DaimlerChrysler)*

2. Start the engine and listen for noises from the power steering system.

   Completed ❑

   Were any noises noticed? _____

   If noises were detected, what could be the source? _____

   _____

   Note: *If you located a power steering system problem while performing Steps 1 and 2, consult your instructor before proceeding with the rest of this job.*

3. Attach a power steering pressure gauge to the pump according to the gauge manufacturer's instructions, **Figure 3.**

   Completed ❑

4. Fill and bleed the power steering system as necessary.

   Completed ❑

5. Measure and record the fluid temperature, if called for by the manufacturer.

   Completed ❑

   Temperature reading: _____

   Specified temperature: _____

   Note: *If the temperature is too low, turn the steering wheel to the right or left full lock position for no more than 5 seconds to heat the fluid.*

Name _____

Torque cylinder line fitting to 18 N•m (13 ft-lb). If leakage persists, replace both O-rings.

If leakage is due to damaged threads, repair fitting nut or replace cylinder line as required. If housing threads are badly damaged, replace housing.

If seepage is observed between torsion bar and stub shaft, replace the valve assembly.

Replace dust and stub shaft seals.

Torque hose fitting to 27 N•m (20 ft-lb). If leakage persists, replace O-ring. If leakage is due to damaged threads, repair fitting nut or replace hose as required. If housing threads are badly damaged, replace housing.

If seepage leak is observed at driver side of housing opening, replace pinion shaft seal.

If leakage is observed at passenger side end, it is necessary to remove bulkhead and replace O-ring seal.

Torque cylinder fitting to 18 N•m (13 ft-lb).

If leakage persists, replace O-ring seal. If leakage is due to damaged threads, repair fitting nut or replace cylinder line. If bulkhead threads are badly damaged, replace bulkhead.

If leakage is observed at cylinder end and spurts when bottomed in left turn, replace the piston rod guide seal and O-ring seal.

Figure 2. *Leak points in a rack-and-pinion system. (Chevrolet)*

6. Start the engine and observe pressure readings with the steering wheel in the straight-ahead position.   Completed ❑

   Pressure reading: _____

   Factory specification: _____

   > Caution: **The following readings should be taken as quickly as possible to avoid overheating the fluid.**

7. With the engine running, observe pressure readings with the steering wheel turned hard right.   Completed ❑

   Pressure reading: _____

   Factory specification: _____

8. With the engine running, observe pressure readings with the steering wheel turned hard left.   Completed ❑

   Pressure reading: _____

   Factory specification: _____

Name _____

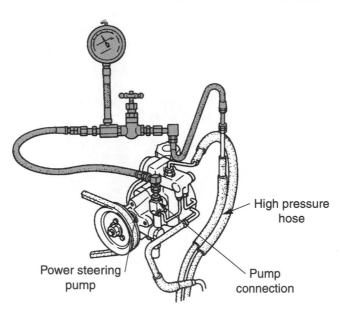

High pressure
hose

Power steering
pump

Pump
connection

Figure 3. *Power steering pressure gauge connected to the high-pressure hose on one particular vehicle. Be sure to follow the manufacturer's instructions when connecting a power steering pressure gauge. (Mazda)*

9. With the engine running, close the pressure gauge valve and observe pressure readings.   Completed ❑

   Pressure reading: _____

   Factory specification: _____

10. Compare readings with factory specifications and determine whether there is a problem in the power steering hydraulic system.   Completed ❑

11. With your instructor's approval, make needed repairs.   Completed ❑

   What repairs were made? _____

   _____

   _____

12. Recheck steering condition.
   Has the problem been corrected? _____ If so, go to Step 13.   Completed ❑

   If the problem still exists, what should you do next?

   _____

   _____

13. Return all tools and equipment to storage and clean the work area.   Completed ❑

14. Did you encounter any problems during this procedure? _____   Completed ❑

   If so, describe the problems and explain what you did to correct them. _____

   _____

   _____

   _____

Name _____ Date _____

Score_____ Instructor _____

Replacing Power Steering System Belts and Hoses

Objective

After studying related textbook material and satisfactorily performing this task, you will be able to remove and replace power steering drive belts and hydraulic hoses.

Materials and Equipment

- Vehicle in need of power steering belt and/or hose replacement
- Replacement parts
- Air-operated tools as needed
- Hand tools as needed
- Correct service literature

> **Warning:** *Before performing this job, review all pertinent safety information in the text and discuss safety procedures with your instructor.*

Procedure

> **Warning:** *Never work on a hot engine. Hot engine parts can cause severe burns. Always allow the engine to cool before performing the following procedures.*

V-Belt Replacement

1. Open the hood and locate the power steering V-belts that require replacement.   Completed ❑

   Why are these components being replaced? _____

   _____

   _____

2. Determine how many other drive belts must be removed before power steering belt can be removed.   Completed ❑

   Total number of belts that must be removed: _____

Name _____

3. Loosen the bolts holding the first belt-driven unit to the engine.

Completed ❑

4. Push the driven unit inward to remove tension from the belt.

Completed ❑

5. Remove the belt.

Completed ❑

6. Repeat Steps 3, 4, and 5 to remove other belts.

Completed ❑

7. Repeat Steps 3, 4, and 5 to remove the power steering pump belt.

Completed ❑

8. Compare the old and new belts.

Completed ❑

  Note: *Even a slight difference in size means the new belt is incorrect.*

9. Place the new belt in position over the power steering pulley.

Completed ❑

10. Pull the power steering pump away from the engine until the proper belt tightness is obtained. See **Figure 1.**

Completed ❑

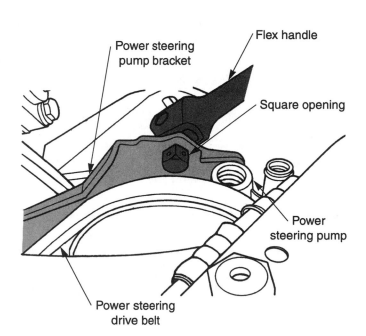

Figure 1. *This power steering pump bracket has an opening for a flex handle. The flex handle can be used to move the bracket and pump when tightening the belt. This eliminates the need to pry on the pump. (DaimlerChrysler)*

11. Tighten the pump fasteners.

Completed ❑

12. Repeat Steps 9, 10, and 11 to install the other belts.

Completed ❑

  How many belts were changed? _____

Name _____

Serpentine Belt Replacement

> Note: *This procedure assumes the vehicle being serviced has one serpentine belt. If more than one belt must be removed, use this procedure or the procedure presented previously, depending on the belt type.*

1. Open the hood and locate the belt that requires replacement.   Completed ❑

   Why are these components being replaced? _____

   _____

   _____

2. Determine whether the engine contains a label showing serpentine belt routing. If not, obtain a service manual showing serpentine belt routing for the vehicle you are servicing.   Completed ❑

3. Locate the belt tensioning device and determine what tools are needed to remove belt tension. See **Figure 2.**   Completed ❑

   List the tool(s) needed to remove belt tension. _____

   _____

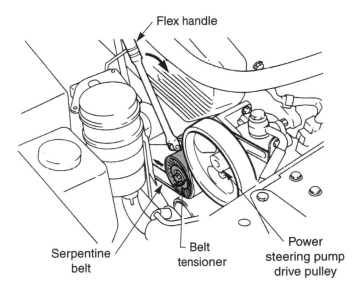

Figure 2. *Typical automatic belt tensioner. In this design, tension can be removed using a flex handle.*

4. Remove tension from the belt using the proper tool.   Completed ❑

5. Remove the serpentine belt from one of the pulleys.   Completed ❑

6. Release the belt tensioning device and remove the belt from the other pulleys.   Completed ❑

7. Compare the new belt to the old belt.   Completed ❑

   > Note: *Even a slight difference in size means the new belt is unusable.*

8. Place the new belt position over all the pulleys except one. Be sure to follow the proper belt routing diagram.   Completed ❑

Name _____

9. Pull the belt tensioning device away from the belt to allow the belt to be installed over the remaining pulley.

Completed ❑

10. Release the tensioning device.

Completed ❑

11. Make sure the belt is properly positioned over the pulleys, **Figure 3.**

Completed ❑

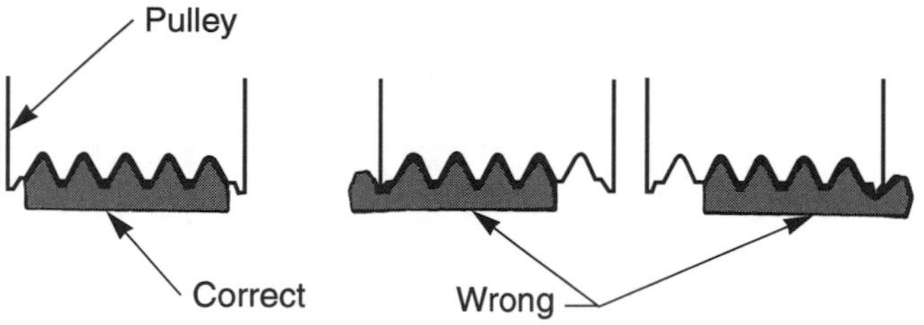

Figure 3. *After installing the belt, check to make sure it is positioned properly on the pulleys. Improperly positioned belts will fail prematurely. (Lexus)*

12. Start the engine and check belt operation.

Completed ❑

Hose Replacement

1. Locate the power steering hoses that require replacement.

Completed ❑

Why are these components being replaced? _____

_____

_____

2. Determine whether any other components must be removed to gain access to the power steering hose.

Completed ❑

List the parts that must be removed. _____

_____

_____

3. Remove any parts that prevent access to the power steering hoses.

Completed ❑

4. Once all obstructing parts are removed, place a drip pan under the power steering hose fittings.

Completed ❑

5. Loosen and remove the hose fittings or clamps. See **Figure 4.**

Completed ❑

6. Remove the hose from the vehicle.

Completed ❑

7. Compare the old and new hoses.

Completed ❑

8. Place the new hose in position and loosely install the fittings.

Completed ❑

9. Make sure the hose will not contact exhaust components or moving parts.

Completed ❑

10. Tighten the hose fittings.

Completed ❑

11. Install any other parts that were removed.

Completed ❑

Name _____

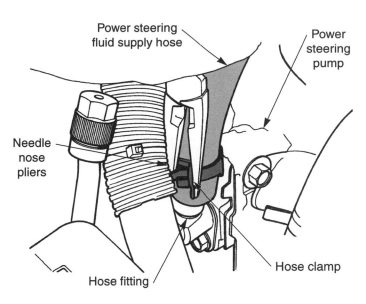

Figure 4. *Using needle nose pliers to remove the power steering supply hose. (Dodge)*

12. Add the appropriate fluid to the power steering reservoir.   Completed ❑

    What type of fluid did you add? _____

13. Check that all tools are removed from the belt area and other moving parts.   Completed ❑

14. Start the engine and bleed the hydraulic system as necessary.   Completed ❑

15. Check belt tightness and system operation.   Completed ❑

16. Return all tools and equipment to storage and clean the work area.   Completed ❑

17. Did you encounter any problems during this procedure? _____   Completed ❑

    If so, describe the problems and explain what you did to correct them. _____

    _____

    _____

    _____

Testing Electronic Suspension and Steering Systems

Objective

After studying related textbook material and satisfactorily performing this task, you will be able to test the operation of electronic suspension and steering systems.

Materials and Equipment

- Vehicle with electronic suspension or steering system
- Correct scan tool
- Hand tools as needed
- Correct service literature

    Warning: *Before performing this job, review all pertinent safety information in the text and discuss safety procedures with your instructor.*

Procedure

1. Start the vehicle and determine whether the suspension or steering warning lights remain on after the engine starts.

    Completed ❑

    Did the warning light remain on after the vehicle was started? _____

2. Listen for noise caused by escaping air.

    Completed ❑

    Were any noises noticed? _____

    If so, what could be the source of the noise? _____

    _____

    Note: *If you located an electronic system problem while performing Steps 1 and 2, consult your instructor before proceeding with the rest of this job.*

Name _____

3. Make a visual inspection for disconnected wires, blown fuses, and damaged components.   Completed ❑

   Were any problems found? _____

   If so, describe the problems. _____

   _____

   _____

4. Make sure the correct cartridge is installed in the scan tool and attach the scan tool to the diagnostic connector. See **Figure 1.**   Completed ❑

   > Note: *Carefully follow the manufacturer's instructions when using a scan tool. Improper hookup or retrieval methods may erase diagnostic trouble codes or damage the control module. Never try to ground or jumper an OBD II connector.*

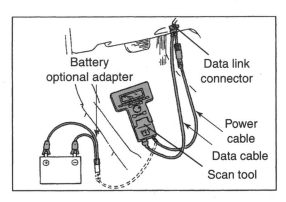

Figure 1. *A proper scan tool hookup will have cable connections to the vehicle's data link connector and, in some cases, to a power source.*

5. Use the scan tool to test the system as necessary.   Completed ❑

   List any trouble codes found. _____

   _____

   What do the trouble codes indicate?

   Code # _____ Problem _____

   Code # _____ Problem _____

   Code # _____ Problem _____

   Code # _____ Problem _____

   Code # _____ Problem _____

   Code # _____ Problem _____

   List any other out-of-specification readings. _____

   _____

   _____

Name _____

6. Study the trouble codes (if any) and scan tool readings   Completed ❑
   to determine whether there is a problem in the elec-
   tronic suspension or steering system. What repairs are
   needed?

   _____

   _____

7. With your instructor's approval, make needed repairs.   Completed ❑

8. Recheck system operation.   Completed ❑

   If the problem was corrected, go to Step 9. If the problem still exists, what should you do next?_____

   _____

   _____

9. Return all tools and equipment to storage and clean   Completed ❑
   the work area.

10. Did you encounter any problems during this   Completed ❑
    procedure? _____

    If so, describe the problems and explain what you did to correct them. _____

   _____

   _____

   _____

Replacing Electronic Suspension and Steering Systems Components

Objective

After studying related textbook material and satisfactorily performing this task, you will be able to remove and replace electronic suspension and steering system parts.

Materials and Equipment

- Vehicle in need of electronic suspension or steering system service
- Replacement parts
- Air-operated tools as needed
- Hand tools as needed
- Correct service literature

> **Warning:** *Before performing this job, review all pertinent safety information in the text and discuss safety procedures with your instructor.*

Procedure

1. Locate the electronic system components in need of replacement.   Completed ❑

   Why are these components being replaced? _____

   _____

   > **Warning:** *Hot engine parts can cause severe burns. Always allow the engine to cool before performing the following procedures.*

2. Open the trunk and turn the control switch to the "off" position.   Completed ❑

3. If necessary, bleed air pressure from the system.   Completed ❑

4. If called for in manufacturer's instructions, attach the scan tool and use it to place the system in standby.   Completed ❑

5. Remove the air lines and/or the electrical connector from the part to be replaced.   Completed ❑

Name _____

6. Remove the fasteners securing the part and remove the part from the vehicle. Some parts may require the removal of linkage.   Completed ❑

7. Compare the old and new parts.   Completed ❑

> **Warning:** *If there is even the slightest doubt as to whether the new part is the correct replacement, do not install it. The incorrect part could cause control module damage or system failure leading to an accident.*

8. Place the new part in position.   Completed ❑

9. Install and tighten the fasteners.   Completed ❑

10. Install all the air lines, linkage, and electrical connectors.   Completed ❑

11. Turn the control switch to the "on" position.   Completed ❑

12. Start the engine and check system operation.   Completed ❑

13. If necessary, adjust the system (ride height adjustment). See **Figure 1.**   Completed ❑

Briefly describe how you performed this procedure. _____

_____

_____

_____

Figure 1. *Some height sensors can be adjusted manually after replacement. On this particular vehicle, loosening the sensor's lock bolt will provide about 5° of actuating arm movement. Each degree of arm movement equals 1/4" (6.35 mm) of ride height travel. (Pontiac)*

14. Return all tools and equipment to storage and clean the work area.   Completed ❑

15. Did you encounter any problems during this procedure? _____   Completed ❑

If so, describe the problems and explain what you did to correct them. _____

_____

_____

_____

Job 15

Performing Two- and Four-Wheel Alignment

Objective

After studying related textbook material and satisfactorily performing this task, you will be able to perform a two- or four-wheel alignment on a car or light truck.

Materials and Equipment

- Vehicle in need of alignment
- Alignment machine and alignment rack
- Lift or floor jack and jack stands
- Alignment adjustment tools as needed
- Hand tools as needed
- Service manuals or other literature as needed

> **Warning:** *Before performing this job, review all pertinent safety information in the text and discuss safety procedures with your instructor.*

Procedure

1. Drive the vehicle onto the alignment rack.   Completed ❑

2. Raise the front of the vehicle so the front suspension is correctly suspended for ball joint checking.   Completed ❑

3. Raise the rear of the vehicle.   Completed ❑

4. Perform the shake test on the front wheels.   Completed ❑

5. If the front wheels appear to have loose parts, check the front suspension and steering parts, wheels and tires for wear or damage.   Completed ❑

   Problems found: _____

   _____

   _____

Name _____

What should you do to correct them? _____

_____

_____

_____

6. Make a visual inspection of the front suspension and
   steering parts.   Completed ❑

   Problems found _____

   _____

   _____

   What should you do to correct them? _____

   _____

   _____

   _____

7. Make a visual inspection of the rear suspension and
   steering parts, as well as the rear wheels and tires.   Completed ❑

8. Check tire condition and pressure and complete the
   following tire condition chart: Completed ❑

Tire	Pressure	Condition
Left front		
Right front		
Right rear		
Left rear		

   Problems found: _____

   _____

   _____

   What should you do to correct them? _____

   _____

   _____

   _____

9. Remove the wheel covers.   Completed ❑

10. Attach the alignment heads to the wheel rims.   Completed ❑

11. If necessary, compensate the heads.   Completed ❑

    Briefly describe how you compensated the heads _____

    _____

    _____

    _____

12. Lock the brake pedal.   Completed ❑

Name _____

13. Observe the camber and toe as displayed on the
alignment machine.   Completed ❑

Record the readings in the following chart:

Alignment Readings			
Left front camber		Right front camber	
Left front toe		Right front toe	
Left rear camber		Right rear camber	
Left rear toe		Right rear toe	

14. Compare the camber and toe readings with
specifications.   Completed ❑

Are readings correct? _____

List any incorrect readings. _____

_____

_____

_____

15. Measure front caster and record the readings: Completed ❑

Front Caster Readings			
Left front caster		Right front caster	

16. Compare the caster readings with specifications.   Completed ❑

Are readings correct? _____

17. Adjust the rear camber and toe as necessary.   Completed ❑

Describe the adjustments made. _____

_____

_____

_____

18. Adjust the front camber and caster as necessary.   Completed ❑

Describe the adjustments made. _____

_____

_____

_____

19. Center and lock the steering wheel.   Completed ❑

20. Adjust the front toe.   Completed ❑

Describe the adjustments made. _____

_____

_____

_____

Name _____

21. Recheck all alignment readings.   Completed ❑

    Are the alignment readings correct? _____

    What should you do next? _____

    _____

    _____

22. Remove alignment heads and store them properly.   Completed ❑

23. Drive the vehicle from the alignment rack.   Completed ❑

24. Road test the vehicle and make sure it drives   Completed ❑
    correctly.

    Check the following during the road test.

        Is the steering wheel centered? _____

        Does the vehicle track correctly (no pulling)? _____

        Does the steering wheel return acceptable? _____

        Is there a minimal amount of road wander? _____

    If the answer to any of the above questions is *no*, what should you do next?

    _____

    _____

25. Return all tools and equipment to storage and clean   Completed ❑
    the work area.

26. Did you encounter any problems during this   Completed ❑
    procedure? _____

    If so, describe the problems and explain what you did to correct them. _____

    _____

    _____

    _____

Performing Suspension and Steering Systems Maintenance

Objective

After studying related textbook material and satisfactorily performing this task, you will be able to perform periodic maintenance on suspension and steering systems.

Materials and Equipment

- Vehicle in need of electronic suspension or steering system maintenance
- Lift or floor jack and jack stands
- Grease gun
- Power steering fluid
- Air-operated tools as needed
- Hand tools as needed
- Correct service literature

> **Warning:** *Before performing this job, review all pertinent safety information in the text and discuss safety procedures with your instructor.*

Procedure

1. Raise the vehicle and locate the steering and suspension lubrication fittings.

   > **Note:** *If the vehicle has rear-wheel drive, check for grease fittings on the drive shaft universal joints.*

   How many fittings are used? _____

   Completed ❑

2. If necessary, remove the fitting plugs and install grease fittings.

   Completed ❑

3. Install the grease gun nozzle on the first fitting.

   Completed ❑

4. Inject grease until the grease seal begins to bulge.

   Completed ❑

5. Repeat Steps 3 and 4 for all the grease fittings.

   Completed ❑

6. If the vehicle is equipped with CV axles, check the boots for tears and signs of lost lubricant.

   Completed ❑

7. Check the fluid level in the power steering reservoir.

   Completed ❑

Name _____

Optional Steps:

Steps 8–21 are to be performed at your instructor's discretion.

8. Place a pan under the power steering reservoir.   Completed ❑

9. Remove the return hose fitting at the reservoir and allow fluid to flow from the reservoir and the return hose into the pan. See **Figure 1.**   Completed ❑

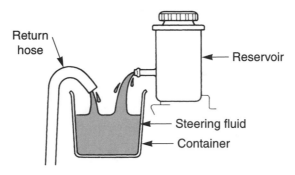

Figure 1. *After removing the return hose from the reservoir, allow the power steering fluid to drain into the container. (Lexus)*

10. Plug the return port and add fluid to the reservoir.   Completed ❑

11. Start the engine and allow the fluid to drain from the return hose into the pan, **Figure 2.** Add clean fluid to the reservoir as the old fluid drains. Continue to add fluid to the reservoir until only clean fluid flows from the return hose.   Completed ❑

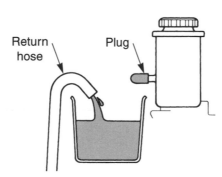

Figure 2. *After plugging the return port and adding fluid to the reservoir, start the engine and allow fluid to flow from the return hose into the pan. (Lexus)*

12. Shut off the engine and remove the plug from the return hose.   Completed ❑

13. Replace the return hose fitting.   Completed ❑

14. Refill the reservoir.   Completed ❑

15. Start the engine.   Completed ❑

16. With the engine running, add fluid to the reservoir until it stabilizes at the full mark.   Completed ❑

Name _____

17. Stop the engine and wait approximately two minutes.   Completed ❑

18. Add fluid to the reservoir, if necessary.   Completed ❑

    What type of fluid was added? _____

19. Start the engine and turn the steering wheel from side   Completed ❑
    to side for about one minute.

    **Caution: *Raise the wheels off the ground or move the vehicle a few feet after
    making each complete turn to avoid rubbing flat spots on the tires.***

20. Repeat Steps 17, 18, and 19 until the fluid has no   Completed ❑
    visible bubbles or foam.

21. Start the engine and check system operation.   Completed ❑

22. Return all tools and equipment to storage and clean   Completed ❑
    the work area.

23. Did you encounter any problems during this   Completed ❑
    procedure? _____

    If so, describe the problems and explain what you did to correct them. _____

    _____

    _____

    _____

Name _____ Date _____

Score _____ Instructor _____

Job 17

Diagnosing Suspension and Steering Problems

Objective

After studying related textbook material and satisfactorily performing this task, you will be able to diagnose steering and suspension problems.

Materials and Equipment

- Vehicle in need of steering and suspension service
- Hand tools, if needed
- Service manuals or other literature
- Replacement parts as needed
- Power steering fluid as needed
- Scan tool as needed
- Pressure gauges and/or micrometers as needed

    Warning: *Before performing this job, review all pertinent safety information in the text and discuss safety procedures with your instructor.*

Procedure

1. Obtain a detailed description of the problem from the vehicle operator.   Completed ❑

2. Obtain the proper service manual for the vehicle.   Completed ❑

3. Road test the vehicle to duplicate the original complaint.   Completed ❑

    What were the results of the road test? _____

    _____

    What do you think is causing the problem (if a problem was detected)?

    _____

    _____

Name _____

Is the problem a brake steering or suspension system defect? _____

Is further action needed? _____

   If yes, go to Step 4. If no, go to Step 9

4. Raise the vehicle and visually and manually check   Completed ❑
   the steering and suspension components, drive axles,
   rims, and tires.

   Describe any defective parts or problem areas found.

   _____

   _____

   _____

   _____

   _____

   _____

   What do these conditions indicate? _____

   _____

   _____

   What should you do next? _____

   _____

   _____

   _____

5. With your instructors approval, make needed repairs   Completed ❑
   or replacements to the steering and suspension
   components, drive axles, rims or tires.

   What repairs did you make? _____

   _____

   _____

6. Recheck system operation.   Completed ❑

   If the system operates correctly, go to Step 7.

   If the problem still exists, what should you do next?

   _____

   _____

7. Return all tools and equipment to storage and clean   Completed ❑
   the work area.

8. Did you encounter any problems during this   Completed ❑
   procedure? _____

   If so, describe the problems and explain what you did to correct them. _____

   _____

   _____

   _____

Name _____ Date _____

Score_____ Instructor _____

Servicing Wheel Bearings

Objective

After studying related textbook material and satisfactorily performing this task, you will be able to clean, lubricate, and adjust tapered wheel bearings, and replace ball and straight roller bearings.

Materials and Equipment

- Vehicle in need of wheel bearing service
- Lift or floor jack and jack stands
- Hand tools as needed
- Wheel bearing grease or appropriate lubricant
- Hydraulic press
- Service manuals or other service literature

    Warning: *Before performing this job, review all pertinent safety information in the text and discuss safety procedures with your instructor.*

Procedure

Servicing Tapered Wheel Bearings

1. Safely raise the vehicle.   Completed ❑

2. Remove the wheel and tire from the vehicle.   Completed ❑

3. On a disc brake system, remove the brake caliper.   Completed ❑

4. Remove the cotter key from the knuckle nut.   Completed ❑

5. Remove the knuckle nut and washer.   Completed ❑

6. Remove the brake drum or rotor and hub.   Completed ❑

7. If necessary, separate the hub from the drum or rotor.   Completed ❑

8. Remove the outer bearing from the hub.   Completed ❑

9. Remove the grease seal from the inner hub and   Completed ❑
   discard it.

    What tool did you use to remove the seal?

_____

Name _____

10. Remove the inner bearing from the hub.   Completed ❑

11. Clean the bearings thoroughly and blow dry.   Completed ❑

12. Inspect the bearings for wear or damage.   Completed ❑
    See **Figure 1.**

    List any signs of bearing damage _____

    _____

    Can this bearing be reused? _____

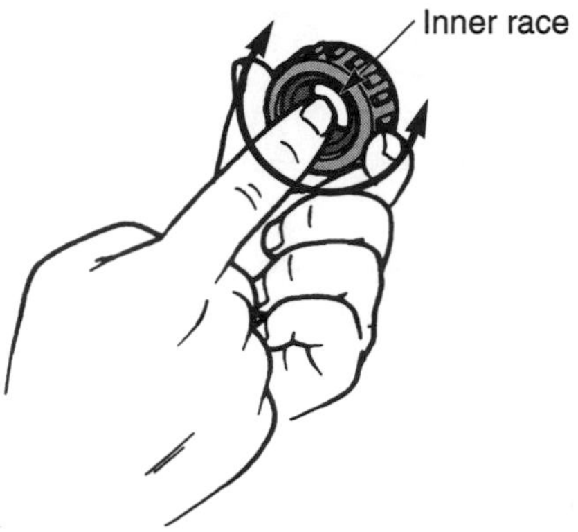

Figure 1. *When checking a tapered wheel bearing for damage, press the bearing tightly into the outer race while turning it. If there is roughness, clean the bearing and retest. If it is still rough, replace the bearing. (Mazda)*

13. Clean the bearing races and the hub interior.   Completed ❑

14. Check the races for wear and damage.   Completed ❑

    List any signs of race damage _____

    _____

    Can this race be reused? _____

15. If a bearing race must be replaced, drive out the old   Completed ❑
    race and install the new race, **Figure 2.**

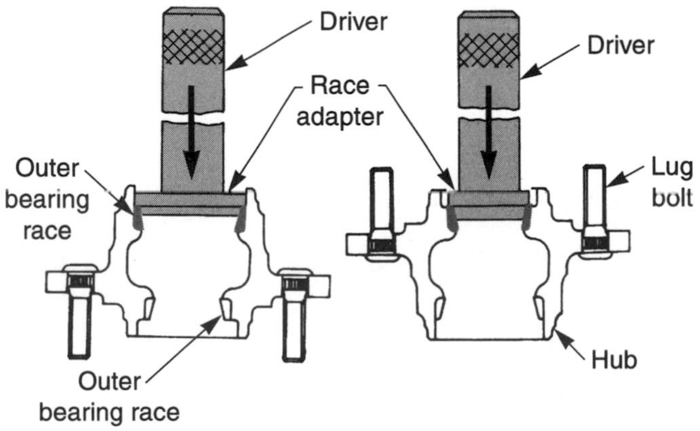

Figure 2. *Installing new bearing races with a bearing race driver. Start the races squarely and make sure they are fully seated. (Hyundai)*

16. Place a small amount of grease in the hub cavity.   Completed ❑

17. Grease the bearings by hand or with a packing tool.   Completed ❑

Name _____

18. Place the inner bearing in the hub and install the new
    seal as shown in **Figure 3.**   Completed ❑

    How did you install the new seal to prevent damage?

    _____

    _____

    _____

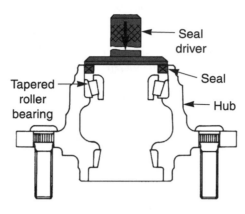

Figure 3. *Using a seal driver to install an oil seal in a hub. Be sure to apply a small amount of grease to the seal lips before installation. (Hyundai)*

19. Clean the knuckle.   Completed ❑

20. Reinstall the hub on the knuckle.   Completed ❑

21. Install the washer and knuckle nut.   Completed ❑

22. Adjust bearing preload.   Completed ❑

    Briefly describe how you set the preload.

    _____

    _____

    _____

23. Install a new cotter pin.   Completed ❑

24. Reinstall the caliper, if necessary.   Completed ❑

25. Reinstall the wheel and tire.   Completed ❑

26. Return all tools and equipment to storage.   Completed ❑

27. Clean the work area.   Completed ❑

    Did you encounter any problems during this procedure? _____

    If so, describe the problems and explain what you did to correct them. _____

    _____

    _____

Replacing Ball or Flat Roller Wheel Bearing used with a CV Axle

1. Obtain the proper service manual for the vehicle.   Completed ❑

2. Safely raise the vehicle.   Completed ❑

Name _____

3. Remove the wheel and tire from the vehicle.   Completed ❑

4. Remove the brake caliper.   Completed ❑

5. If used, remove the cotter key from the CV axle nut.   Completed ❑

6. Remove the axle nut and washer. Disconnect the   Completed ❑
   antilock brake wheel speed sensor, if necessary.

7. Separate the CV axle drive shaft from the hub.   Completed ❑
   > Note: *This may require the use of a removal tool.*

8. Support the suspension under the control arms.   Completed ❑
   > Warning: *Do not remove any suspension fasteners until you are sure all spring*
   > *tension has been removed. Have your instructor check the vehicle before*
   > *proceeding.*

   All spring tension has been removed. _____

   Checked by instructor or other qualified person. _____

9. Remove the tie rod end from the knuckle.   Completed ❑

10. Remove the ball joint(s) and/or strut bolts from the   Completed ❑
    knuckle.

11. Remove the knuckle assembly from the vehicle.   Completed ❑

12. Remove any dust shields and seals from the inboard   Completed ❑
    side of the knuckle.

13. Remove any snap rings holding the bearings in the   Completed ❑
    knuckle.

14. Place the knuckle assembly in a suitable press.   Completed ❑

15. Using the proper adapters, press the bearing from the   Completed ❑
    knuckle. See **Figure 4.**

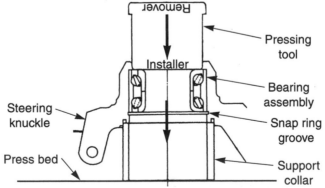

Figure 4. *A special pressing tool and a support collar are used when pressing the bearing assembly from the knuckle.*
(General Motors)

16. Compare the old and new bearings.   Completed ❑

    Is the new bearing a correct replacement for the old bearing? _____

    If not, what should be done? _____

    _____

    _____

Name _____

17. Using the proper adapters, press the new bearing into the knuckle.   Completed ❑

18. Replace any snap rings, seals, and dust shields. See **Figure 5.**   Completed ❑

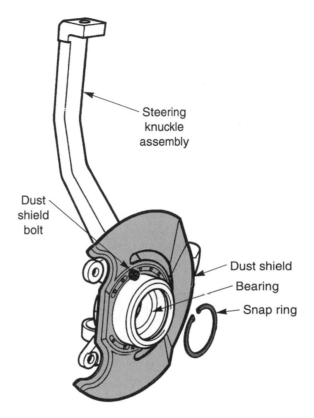

Figure 5. *Dust shield and snap ring orientation on one particular vehicle. When installing the snap ring, make sure it is completely seated in its groove. (Sterling)*

19. Reinstall the knuckle on the vehicle.   Completed ❑

20. Install and tighten the ball joint fasteners and install new cotter pins.   Completed ❑

21. Install the tie rod end and install a new cotter pin.   Completed ❑

22. Reinstall the CV axle shaft nut and washer.   Completed ❑

23. Reinstall the wheel and tire.   Completed ❑

24. Return all tools and equipment to storage and clean the work area.   Completed ❑

25. Did you encounter any problems during this procedure? _____   Completed ❑

    If so, describe the problems and explain what you did to correct them. _____

    _____

    _____

Name _____

Replacing Ball or Flat Roller Wheel Bearing used with a Solid Rear Axle

1. Obtain the proper service manual for the vehicle.   Completed ❑

2. Safely raise the vehicle.   Completed ❑

3. Remove the wheel and tire from the vehicle.   Completed ❑

4. Remove the drum or brake caliper.   Completed ❑

5. Determine whether the axle is held to the housing   Completed ❑
   with a retainer plate or a C-lock.

   Retainer plate ___   C-lock ____

6. Remove the retainer plate bolts or the differential   Completed ❑
   cover and C-lock as applicable.

7. Remove the axle shaft from the housing.   Completed ❑

8. Determine whether the bearing is pressed on the shaft   Completed ❑
   or installed in the housing.

   On shaft ___ Go to Step 9.

   In housing ___ Go to Step 13.

9. Use a grinder and a chisel to remove the retaining   Completed ❑
   collar from the shaft. See **Figure 6.**

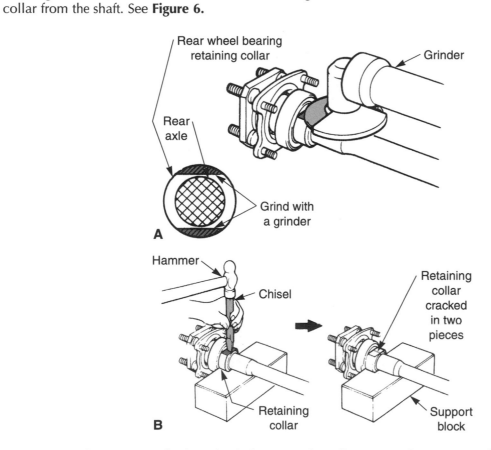

Figure 6. *Removing the retaining collar from the shaft. A—Grind two flat spots on the retaining collar. B—Split the collar on the ground flats with a hammer and chisel. (General Motors)*

Name _____

10. Using suitable adapters, press the bearing from the shaft.   Completed ❑

11. Press the new bearing on the shaft after first placing the retainer plate on the shaft.   Completed ❑

12. Press the new retaining collar over the bearing, then go to Step 17.   Completed ❑

13. Remove the outer axle seal.   Completed ❑

14. Remove the snap ring holding the bearing in the axle housing.   Completed ❑

15. Remove the bearing from the housing.   Completed ❑

> Note: *Most bearings are loosely installed in the housing, but oil deposits may cause them to stick. If necessary, use a slide hammer to remove the bearing.*

16. Install a new bearing and seal. See **Figure 7.**   Completed ❑

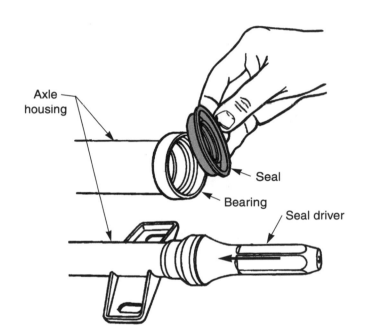

Figure 7. *Installing a new seal in the axle housing. Use the correct seal driver to prevent damage. (General Motors)*

17. Reinstall the shaft in the housing.   Completed ❑

18. Install the retainer plate or C-lock.   Completed ❑

19. If necessary, reinstall the differential cover using a new gasket and add the proper amount of new gear oil.   Completed ❑

20. Make sure the axle shaft turns freely.   Completed ❑

21. Reinstall the wheel and tire.   Completed ❑

22. Return all tools and equipment to storage and clean the work area.   Completed ❑

23. Did you encounter any problems during this procedure? _____   Completed ❏

If so, describe the problems and explain what you did to correct them. _____

_____

_____

Servicing Drive Shafts and CV Axles

Objective

After studying related textbook material and satisfactorily performing this task, you will be able to service rear-wheel drive drive shafts and front-wheel drive CV axles.

Materials and Equipment

- Vehicle in need of drive shaft or CV axle service
- Lift or floor jack and jack stands
- Replacement parts
- Air-operated tools as needed
- Hand tools as needed
- Correct service literature

    Warning: *Before performing this job, review all pertinent safety information in the text and discuss safety procedures with your instructor.*

Procedure

Drive Shaft Service

1. Safely raise the vehicle.   Completed ❑

2. Remove the fasteners holding the rear of the drive shaft to the pinion flange.   Completed ❑

    What kind of fasteners hold the rear of the drive shaft to the pinion?

    _____

    _____

    Is this a one-piece or two-piece drive shaft? _____

3. If necessary remove the center support bolts.   Completed ❑

4. Push the drive shaft forward to clear the pinion flange.   Completed ❑

5. Remove the drive shaft from the transmission.   Completed ❑

Name _____

6. Clamp the drive shaft lightly in a vise.   Completed ❑

7. Remove the retainers holding the U-joint to the drive   Completed ❑
    shaft yoke. See **Figure 1.**

    Describe the retainers. _____

    How did you remove them? _____

    _____

    _____

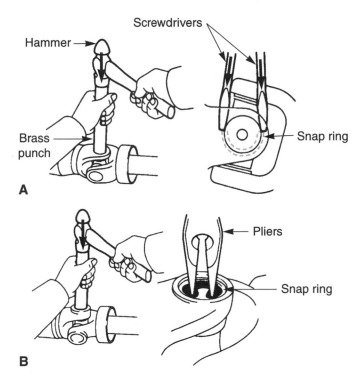

Figure 1. *A—On a universal joint with an internal snap ring, tap the bearing cap inward slightly and remove the snap ring with two screwdrivers. B—On a joint with an external snap ring, gently tap the bearing cap inward; then use pliers to remove the ring. (Toyota)*

8. Use a vise or press and the proper size drivers to   Completed ❑
    remove the bearing caps from the drive shaft yoke(s).

9. Reassemble the U-joint.   Completed ❑

10. Install the new U-joint in the drive shaft yoke.   Completed ❑

11. Install the U-joint snap rings.   Completed ❑

    Did you have difficulty getting the snap rings to seat? _____

    If so, what was the cause? _____

    _____

12. Install the drive shaft in the rear of the transmission.   Completed ❑

13. Install the drive shaft on the pinion flange.   Completed ❑

14. Install and tighten the drive shaft fasteners.   Completed ❑

15. Lower the vehicle and check drive shaft operation.   Completed ❑

Name _____

16. Return all tools and equipment to storage and clean the work area.   Completed ❑

17. Did you encounter any problems during this procedure? _____   Completed ❑

    If so, describe the problems and explain what you did to correct them. _____

    _____

    _____

    _____

CV Axle Service

1. Safely raise the vehicle.   Completed ❑

2. Remove the wheel on the side of the CV axle to be removed.   Completed ❑

   Which side is to be serviced? _____

   Does this axle have an intermediate shaft? _____

3. Remove the center nut holding the CV axle to the hub.   Completed ❑

4. Remove the necessary suspension parts to gain axle clearance.   Completed ❑

5. Remove the CV axle from the steering knuckle hub. See **Figure 2.**   Completed ❑

   Is a special tool needed to remove the shaft from the hub? _____

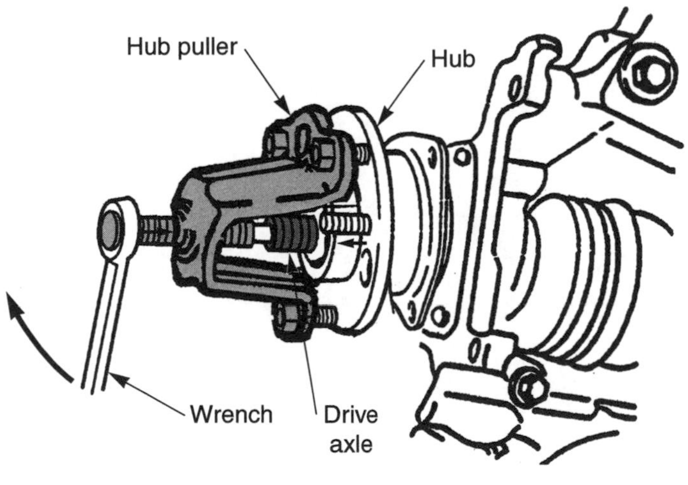

Figure 2. *Using a puller to separate the hub and drive axle. Follow the manufacturer's recommendations. (Pontiac)*

6. Remove the CV axle from the transaxle.   Completed ❑

7. Clamp the CV axle lightly in a vise.   Completed ❑

8. Remove the clamps holding CV joint boot and remove the boot.   Completed ❑

Name _____

9. Disassemble the CV joint as needed.   Completed ❑

    Is the CV joint a Rzeppa or tripod type? _____

10. Check all internal parts for wear and damage.   Completed ❑

11. Obtain new parts as needed.   Completed ❑

12. Reassemble the CV joint.   Completed ❑

13. Add sufficient lubricant of the proper type.   Completed ❑

         Caution: *Do not use chassis grease in a CV joint.*

14. Install the CV boot using new clamps.   Completed ❑

15. Install the CV axle in the transaxle.   Completed ❑

16. Install the CV axle in the steering knuckle.   Completed ❑

17. Reassemble the front suspension as necessary.   Completed ❑

18. Install and tighten the CV axle nut.   Completed ❑

19. Install the wheel and tire.   Completed ❑

20. Lower the vehicle and check CV axle operation.   Completed ❑

21. Return all tools and equipment to storage and clean   Completed ❑
    the work area.

22. Did you encounter any problems during this   Completed ❑
    procedure? _____

    If so, describe the problems and explain what you did to correct them. _____

    _____

    _____

    _____

Name _____ Date _____

Score_____ Instructor _____

Replacing Wheel Studs

Objective

After studying related textbook material and satisfactorily performing this task, you will be able to replace a wheel stud.

Materials and Equipment

- Vehicle in need of wheel stud replacement
- Lift or floor jack and jack stands
- Replacement stud
- Air-operated tools as needed
- Hand tools as needed
- Correct service literature

> **Warning:** *Before performing this job, review all pertinent safety information in the text and discuss safety procedures with your instructor.*

Procedure

1. Safely raise the vehicle.   Completed ❑

   Which wheel contains the damaged stud? _____

2. Remove the wheel and tire.   Completed ❑

3. Knock out the damaged stud with a large hammer or a stud removal tool, **Figure 1.**   Completed ❑

4. Remove the damaged stud from the vehicle.   Completed ❑

   > **Note:** *If necessary, remove the rotor and splash shield to allow the stud to be removed from the rear of the wheel assembly.*

5. Compare the old and new studs.   Completed ❑

   > **Note:** *If the studs do not match, obtain the correct stud before proceeding. Do not attempt to install an incorrect stud.*

6. Place the new stud in position on the hub.   Completed ❑

7. Lubricate the stud threads.   Completed ❑

Name _____

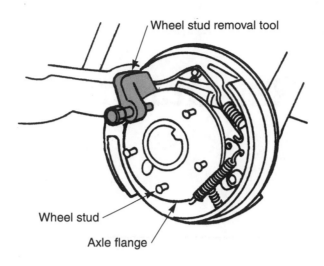

Figure 1. *A special tool can be used to press out a damaged stud. (General Motors)*

8. Install washers and a lug nut on the stud. See **Figure 2.**   Completed ❏

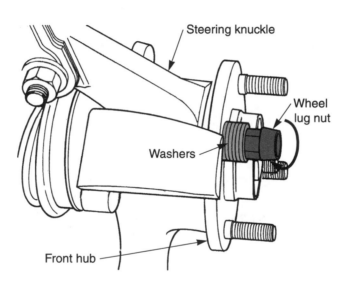

Figure 2. *To install a new wheel stud in the flange, place washers over the stud and run up the flat side of the lug nut to the washers. Tighten the lug nut to pull the stud into position.*

9. Slowly tighten the nut to draw the stud into the hub.   Completed ❏

10. Check that the stud is fully seated in the hub.   Completed ❏

11. Remove the nut and washers from the stud.   Completed ❏

12. Install the wheel and tire.   Completed ❏

13. Return all tools and equipment to storage and clean the work area.   Completed ❏

14. Did you encounter any problems during this procedure? _____   Completed ❏

   If so, describe the problems and explain what you did to correct them. _____

   _____

   _____

Name _____ Date _____

Score _____ Instructor _____

Overhauling Manual or Power Steering Gears

Objective

After studying related textbook material and satisfactorily completing this job, you will be able to overhaul a manual or power steering gear.

Materials and Equipment

- Steering gear in need of overhaul
- Replacement parts
- Air-operated tools as needed
- Hand tools as needed
- Correct service literature

  Warning: *Before performing this job, review all pertinent safety information in the text and discuss safety procedures with your instructor.*

Procedure

Note: *Because of the large number of steering gears in use, this procedure is general in scope. Always consult the proper service manual before proceeding. This procedure can be used to overhaul a steering gear installed on a vehicle or on a bench unit.*

1. Remove the steering gear from the vehicle, if necessary.   Completed ❑

2. Place the steering gear on a clean bench.   Completed ❑

   Who is the manufacturer of the steering gear? _____

3. Remove the sector gear cover (side cover) or remove the inner tie rod ends.   Completed ❑

4. Remove the worm or pinion shaft retainer.
   See **Figure 1.**   Completed ❑

5. Remove the worm or pinion shaft and power steering control valve, if used.   Completed ❑

6. Remove other internal parts from the gearbox.   Completed ❑

Name _____

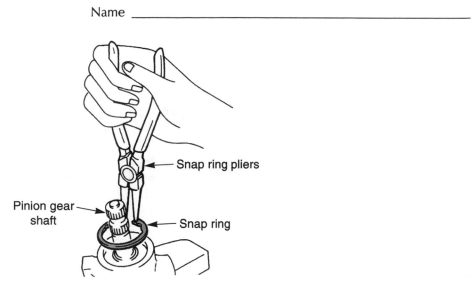

Figure 1. *Removing the pinion shaft snap ring with snap ring pliers.*

7. Inspect all parts for wear and damage, **Figure 2.**   Completed ❑

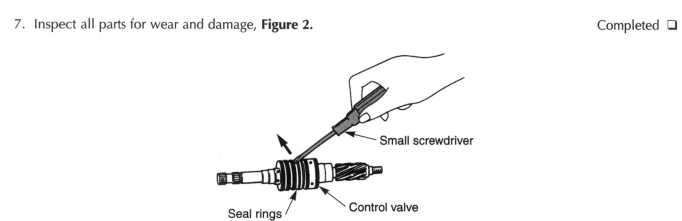

Figure 2. *To check the condition of the control valve sealing rings, carefully remove the rings with a small screwdriver. If the sealing rings are worn or cut, they must be replaced.*

8. Obtain new parts as needed.   Completed ❑

Name some parts that should always be replaced during an overhaul.

_____

_____

_____

_____

9. Lightly lubricate all internal parts with the proper   Completed ❑
    lubricant.

10. Assemble the gear using the new parts.   Completed ❑

11. After assembly, check the gear for free movement.   Completed ❑

12. Reinstall the gear on the vehicle, if necessary.   Completed ❑

13. If the unit is installed on a vehicle, bleed the system   Completed ❑
    and check operation.

14. Return all tools and equipment to storage and clean   Completed ❑
    the work area.

Name _____

15. Did you encounter any problems during this   Completed ❑
    procedure? _____

    If so, describe the problems and explain what you did to correct them. _____

    _____

    _____

    _____

Overhauling a Power Steering Pump

Objective

After studying related textbook material and satisfactorily performing this task, you will be able to overhaul a power steering pump.

Materials and Equipment

- Power steering pump in need of overhaul
- Replacement parts
- Air-operated tools as needed
- Hand tools as needed
- Correct service literature

> **Warning:** *Before performing this job, review all pertinent safety information in the text and discuss safety procedures with your instructor.*

Procedure

> **Note:** *The following procedure can be used to overhaul a power steering pump installed on a vehicle or a bench unit. Always consult the proper service manual before proceeding.*

1. Remove the pump from the vehicle, if necessary.   Completed ❑

2. Place the pump on a clean bench.   Completed ❑

   The manufacturer of this pump is _____.

3. Remove the pump reservoir, if used. See **Figure 1.**   Completed ❑

4. Disassemble the pump.   Completed ❑

5. Inspect all internal parts for wear and damage.   Completed ❑

6. Obtain new parts as needed.   Completed ❑

   Name the parts that should always be replaced during a power steering pump overhaul.

   _____

   _____

   _____

Name _____

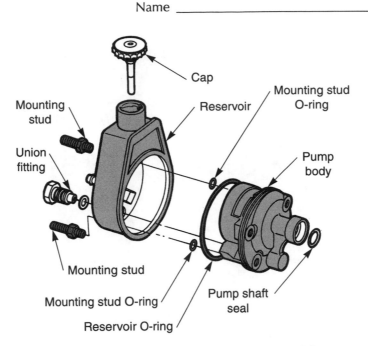

Figure 1. *To remove the reservoir on this particular pump, remove the hose fittings and the mounting studs that hold the reservoir to the pump. Then gently pry the reservoir from the pump body. (DaimlerChrysler)*

7. Lightly lubricate all internal parts with the proper lubricant.   Completed ❑

8. Assemble the pump using the new parts.   Completed ❑

9. After assembly, check that the pump turns freely.   Completed ❑

10. Reinstall the reservoir on the pump, if necessary.   Completed ❑

11. Reinstall the pump on the vehicle, if necessary.   Completed ❑

12. If the unit is installed on a vehicle, bleed the system and check operation.   Completed ❑

13. Return all tools and equipment to storage and clean the work area.   Completed ❑

14. Did you encounter any problems during this procedure? _____   Completed ❑

    If so, describe the problems and explain what you did to correct them. _____

    _____

    _____

    _____